A Peasant's Diary

A Peasant's Diary

Robin Page

ROBINSON PUBLISHING
London

Robinson Publishing
7, Kensington Church Court
London W8 4SP

First published by Robinson Publishing 1993

A copy of the British Library Cataloguing in Publication
Data for this title is available from the British Library.

ISBN 1–85487–243–5

Typeset by Hewer Text Composition, Edinburgh
Printed and bound in Great Britain by
Biddles Ltd, Guildford and King's Lynn

Contents

For my dog Bramble.
Every true peasant
Should have at least one.

Introduction

This Peasant's Diary is a collection of my fortnightly Farmer's Diary articles in the *Daily Telegraph*. There is one slight difference however – this volume is unexpurgated. A newspaper column can vary in length from week to week, depending on news stories, disasters, and advertising. Consequently some weeks my 'diary' appears as written, on others it will shrink, according to the space available. With a book there is no competition and so there are many gems and disasters that are recorded here for the first time. In addition I have written a number of chapters especially for the book and so regular readers of the *Daily Telegraph* will read much new material as well as the old. There are also two pieces included that have appeared in *Country Living* magazine.

I would like to thank both publications for permission to reproduce the articles in book form.

For a lifestyle like mine thanks are due to several people. As readers will quickly see I owe my father much gratitude for all the material he has given me, as well as for his friendship. I am grateful to my mother too for all her help and advice, and for the number of times she feeds me and looks after my dog. I am rather worried by her admiration for the former Secretary of State for Agriculture – but we all have our blind spots. To my brother thanks for accepting that I have to spend much time ploughing an unknown furrow with my pen. The same thanks must be extended to my sister-in-law Ellen, and to her litter – Edwin and Lena.

My sister Rachael checked the proofs which was another great help. I must also thank the Rt. Hon John Selwyn Gummer MP, who was Secretary of State for Agriculture during the time covered by this Peasant's Diary – he caused me much amusement and amazement.

Finally I would like to thank my dog Bramble. For some reason he managed to keep flea-free during the typing of this document which made the whole process much easier than it could have been.

1

The Last of the English Peasants

My father was a farmer. I am a peasant. Tomorrow I could be an endangered species. I am not complaining, as I actually enjoy being a peasant and feel it to be my true vocation. But for some strange reason modern-day Britain does not seem to like peasants, or even want them. In fact there is nothing wrong with being a peasant; I started being one as soon as I arrived in the cottage where I was born – approximately ten feet away from where I am writing this diary. I was the second son, the third child, of parents who both worked on our small farm to keep us.

My clothes were second hand, even third hand, my bike was not new and my mother 'mended and made do'. I still have the same philosophy, and although I buy my clothes new, I wear them until they fall to pieces.

Some of my earliest memories involve the farm: helping to collect the eggs, feeding the young calves and watching seed time and harvest. The seasons and the soil were all-important. As I got older I took part in the harvest. Since those days my pen has become an additional tool, but even if I have to travel to write, I always return for springtime and harvest.

The history of the peasant is an honourable one. For generations the yeoman peasant was the backbone of England. Hard working, dependable and loyal. Now those people with mud on their boots and straw in their hair are regarded as inferior – and if they have a rural accent, stupid as well. Although being a peasant is enjoyable, and fulfilling, the public perception is of a semi-literate, inbred bumpkin, living in squalor. The fact that to be a peasant you have to live in the country is the cause of the problem, for these days most people who live in the towns would rather be living in the country, and they don't want strange country people living next to them.

1

They want peace and quiet in which to have their Sunday morning 'drinks' parties and their houses must have large drives so that the central-heating oil lorry can get to the storage tank without scratching the BMW. To have people with smelly hens next door, who burn smoky logs and who throw manure onto their gardens and then eat the vegetables that grow through, is just not on.

Fortunately the 'free market' has come to the aid of the incomers, for house prices have become so high that many country people cannot afford to buy. This means that the rustics have to move into the towns for cheaper housing and the wealthier townspeople can move out into the country, for more expensive housing – it is bizarre.

To make it more absurd, once some of the townspeople have moved into the country, they then attempt to make their bit of country more like town, with concrete forecourts instead of gardens, improved street-lighting, double yellow lines, and a ban on all things that bark, moo, grunt, or turn grass into droppings of various shapes, sizes and colours.

As a result the remnant of the genuine country population has been showered with assorted writs, together with summonses and edicts from local and national governments. Country things and country people are really not wanted in the countryside. Last year an old countryman had to appear in court as his cockerel's crowing was waking his neighbour – ex-London – every morning at dawn. The question of urban insomnia did not arise.

Elsewhere a dairy farmer received a solicitor's letter because of his cows. As he drove them along the road each day they rubbed against a neighbour's large privet hedge, to brush off flies. Oh what a crime. Another peasant farmer was instructed to remove his scarecrows. Holding broom handles they had frightened another ex-urban dweller who thought they were men with guns. What a naughty farmer, and who cares about protecting his crops – he had frightened a poor innocent rambler. Alas, it is not recorded what the scarecrows felt on seeing the woman. With absurdities such as these, perhaps Britain should be renamed Fantasy Island.

Now the Ministry of Agriculture appears to have joined in the fun: its main policy seems to be to get as many people off the land as quickly as possible, and it seems to be succeeding. As people in towns and industry expect wage increases each year, the Ministry, with help from the European Community, has come up with the novel idea of reducing the incomes of farmers. It is working very well and as a result thousands of farmers and workers are being forced off the land. In addition, 200 farmers a year are committing suicide. With such a successful plan the Ministry officials can expect a selection of OBEs, MBEs and Knighthoods as a reward.

Sadly, small was once considered to be beautiful, now it is an inconvenience. The politicians want the land to be in large blocks, in as few hands as possible. They want agriculture to be a matter of production control carried out by land managers; farmers and peasants who regard food production and care for the land as a way of life are redundant and inconvenient.

Fortunately I am not redundant and I enjoy being inconvenient. I enjoy other things too that the bureaucrats cannot understand. I have no desire for a BMW; I do not possess a CD player or a washing-up machine. I do not want to go to the Canary Islands in January, or to Bermuda in April. I already have what I want and most of my most treasured possessions are in fact free: the larks singing in the spring; butterflies in the hay meadow and the footprints of a fox over frosted grass.

But the peasant has something else too that others both envy and fear; it is independence. I suppose that is really what worries the bureaucrats.

2

A Woolly Jumper

Every evening at the moment I walk into the dusk to check the
sheep. There have been some spectacular sunsets lately with colour
filling the whole of the south-western portion of our lowland sky;
first yellow, then red, crimson and finally a darkening purple. It
is on evenings like these that I am glad we have no mountains to
block out the view.

The sheep are grazing on old water meadows that now seldom
flood. As I approach they always run to me and one ewe, Leah,
invariably jumps the three strands of electric wire to greet me. I
like friendly animals, but a genuine woolly jumper, that will jump
out of a field and then take fifteen minutes before she condescends
to jump back in again, is being rather too friendly.

By the time I walk back to the farm, darkness has fallen. In the
heart of the country it should be a time of peace and quiet, but these
days with roads on three sides I can hear cars all the time; there are
usually the lights of three or four aircraft above – and sometimes
there are as many as seven adding to the intrusion. Then, to make
matters worse, there are distant street lights and the orange glows of
a factory, a plant-breeding institute and a garage. It is continual light
and sound pollution: part of the joy of country living has been taken
away, with no compensation from the airport lobby, the motorway
builders, or the electricity companies.

I hate touching electric fences and would never dream of touching
the sheep fence to test the current. My old father is different; he will
hold it and, despite his slightly twitching arm, will claim to hardly
feel the pulses of electricity. The other day as we leaned on a metal
sheep hurdle by the fence, I asked him to test the current. Without
thinking he grabbed the wire while still holding the metal hurdle.

4

The current rushed to earth, through him; there was a fizz and a spark and he jumped backwards; his woolly bobble hat went high into the air and the icicle on the end of his nose went even higher. 'Yes', he said, 'it's still on.'

The other afternoon I went to check the sheep early and let two of the dogs, Bramble and Rinty, hunt the banks of the brook as we went. Bramble is my dog, a little lurcher with a good memory, and he ran straight to the spot amid blackthorn and hawthorn bushes where they had flushed a fox two days before. This time he flushed something else, with beautiful long, brown and mottled wings that flapped and glided silently. The birds flew right by me – five long-eared owls – before diving into more thicket. They were the first long-eared owls I had seen for twenty years, and the first I had ever seen on the farm. Another remained perching, sitting strangely upright and looking thin, as they do when they are worried.

I have been back to that area of the brook several times since, with my battered binoculars and without the dogs, and enjoyed excellent, undisturbed views. They are smaller than I had remembered (13½ inches), being smaller than the tawny, but they must be our most beautiful owl, even more attractive than the barn owl, with large orange-yellow eyes and two feather tufts – their 'ears'. Apparently they often spend their winters in little groups. This gang is almost certainly hunting a forty acre patch of rough set-aside along the far bank of the brook. They are yet another of the wildlife pluses of set-aside. If just a little more thought had been given to the whole set-aside scheme, wildlife could have benefited so greatly . . .

Twenty years ago the old water meadows would often disappear under water during the winter and when it froze they became ideal for skating. This year the frosts have been frustrating, never quite severe enough for ice to bear. I keep getting my skates out, only for a twenty-four hour thaw to get them back into the cupboard again. Before Christmas, when the ice was thick, it took all the local skaters by surprise. Normally in such weather a large fen field is flooded, but when it came early, bullocks were still grazing and the water was kept out. I hope this year that the old adage is right and that 'as the days lengthen', the cold really does 'strengthen', so that my skates can actually be used.

3

Christmas Greetings

It seems only last week that Christmas was being celebrated; now Christmas is on us again already. Fortunately I am prepared; if anybody doubts my word, I still have two tasteful lengths of green string stretched between pictures on my sitting room wall. They are last year's Christmas card holders; ever since Twelfth Night I have been meaning to take them down, but now I will just have to leave them up for this year's cards.

I enjoy Christmas and the Christian message of hope that goes with it. What I object to is the over-commercialization of Christmas, which seems to get worse every year. I saw my first shop selling Christmas cards in June, and by September there were several more urging 'Shop Early for Christmas'. None of them received my custom.

The poor Biblical knowledge of some of our bishops never fails to amaze me. Usually at this time of year there appears a gaggle of trendy clerics talking about the deprived and the unemployed in our inner cities, and how Jesus went looking for them during his ministry. They are wrong, of course. Jesus was a countryman, born in a stable, and actually the people flocked to him, usually in the countryside.

In fact, because Jesus was a countryman there is much country lore and wisdom in the Bible, as well as numerous insights into the wildlife of the Middle East at that time. A version of one of our commonest pieces of weather lore can also be found in St Matthew's Gospel. We say: 'Red sky at night, shepherd's delight; red sky in the morning, shepherd's warning'. According to St Matthew (16: 2–3), Jesus said: 'When it is evening, ye say, it will be fair weather, for the sky is red. And in the morning, it will be foul weather today, for the sky is red and lowering.'

* * *

Although for most people the build up to Christmas is an enjoyable time, for postmen it is a nightmare. At one time, before my pen-nib was as active as it is today, I worked as a part-time postman for an hour-and-a-half each day. I enjoyed my stint as a postman, cycling around the village every morning. On several occasions I met foxes in the High Street, and one morning there was actually one sitting outside the door of the Post Office.

A village postman cannot fail to learn almost all there is to know about his fellow villagers. He discovers who has investments; who has been summonsed; who receives electricity demands in red, and who comes out of the wrong house first thing in the morning. I often had little messages put on postcards for me to read, but I always pretended that I did not see them. In view of his informed position in village society, it has always surprised me that a postman is not one of the main characters in 'The Archers'.

Most country postmen are friendly, easy-going people. It is significant that in any industrial dispute, the country postmen are last out on strike and first back. The last back are usually those from London, Glasgow, Manchester and Cardiff. People who talk about the North–South divide are wrong; the greatest divide of all is between urban and rural. It always has been and I expect it always will be.

I met a young post office inspector the other day, fresh out of university. He was in charge of accident reports and was puzzled. He claimed that most of the reports he had to read from postmen who crashed their vans were, at best, semi-literate. Worse still, he said, many of them seemed hardly able to read. That explains why a selection of my mail goes to Lincolnshire, Bedfordshire and Humberside. How can Barton, Cambridgeshire be confused with Barton-upon-Humber? The much vaunted post-code seems to make no difference; in fact, I have stopped using it. I object to being a number anyway.

On Boxing Day I shall probably watch the meet of the Cambridge-shire Hunt. I do not normally hunt, but I like to see this old and very picturesque tradition continued. Many urban and suburban dwellers fail to see the place of fox-hunting in country life and want to ban it. Sadly the genuine countryman and the things he enjoys are becoming increasingly misunderstood. As I see my village and lifestyle change, quite against my will, there are times when I feel like a member of a neglected ethnic minority, but nobody seems to care. There are no organizations fighting to ensure my welfare, and there are times when I feel that I am fighting a losing battle.

I hope the 'antis' are not at the Boxing day meet. I have met many in my time; a few I admire, but most I have found rather tedious. Their anti-hunting stance seems to be more a political statement about the 'class war' rather than a real concern for foxes and conservation.

Two years ago, in the drizzle, I asked a local if there were any 'antis' present. He was a keen car follower – born with a muck shovel in his mouth rather than a silver spoon. His answer was enlightening: 'There won't be any out today', he replied, 'the rain would make the colours in their hair run.'

Last year's meet was also exciting. I volunteered to borrow a horse-box and take my niece and cousin on their first hunt. It was also my first time with a horse-box in tow. 'No problem', I announced grandly, 'farmers can handle trailers better than ordinary people.' As it turned out I could also back into a festive red Nissan better than most ordinary people. It was rather an expensive Christmas – I hope it will be dent-free, and cheaper, this year.

4

It's a Pig's Life

One of the most attractive animals on the farm is Snowdrop, a large Middle White sow. She is a very special animal, for not only is she pedigree, but she is also a Rare Breed. She is beautiful too, if you like that sort of thing; she reminds me rather of Roy Hattersley after a particularly good meal. Some of the breed's ancestry comes from China, which shows in her eyes and her chubby face. The other Chinese similarity is that she has been a prolific breeder.

All her offspring so far have been crossbred; delivered by artificial insemination. But now, to keep the line going, we want to breed her pure and this has been a problem – the nearest pure bred boar, in good working order, is sixty miles away, just off the M25, at Iver, in Buckinghamshire.

So first of all we wanted a licence to move her, as in farming these days you need a licence, or completed forms in triplicate, for almost everything. But we could not remember where the licences came from. I phoned the headquarters of the Cambridgeshire County Council with the simple request: 'I would like a licence to move a sow please', and for anybody in doubt a sow is a female pig, or in modern parlance a 'ms pig'. 'What?' came the bemused reply, 'You want a what?' After a brief explanation I was informed: 'You should try the Ministry of Agriculture.'

Sadly the Min. of Ag. was no better; to my simple question came the familiar reply: 'What? – you want to what? You should try the Min. of Ag. Huntingdon.' By now the Huntingdon telephonist's reply was no surprise: 'What? – You want to what?' 'I want to move a sow.' 'What's a sow?' (I wonder if her surname was Gummer.) 'I want to take a mummy pig to see a daddy pig', I explained in exasperation.

Finally the message hit home, I had got the wrong department.

'Where should I go?', I asked. 'Cambridgeshire County Council', came the reply. Finally somebody at the County Council directed me to the correct office – the Trading Standards Department. How silly of me, I should have known. The licence was obtained and in an old borrowed Land Rover, with Snowdrop apparently asleep in an equally old horse box, we set off for the M25, with me at the wheel and father as navigator. After three miles I looked in the mirror: I was shocked. At first I thought that Roy Hattersley was hotfooting it after us, but it was Snowdrop, now fully awake and wanting to go for a walk. With her hard head she had smashed the front door of the horse trailer and was about to jump.

I screeched to a halt. Father floundered about, all arms and legs, deperately trying to get out. He had forgotten to undo his seatbelt. Just in time, as a Danish bacon container lorry rushed past, Snowdrop was persuaded to proceed no further. There was only one thing for it – retreat. Snowdrop loose on the M25 would not have been a good thing. So holding the damaged door shut with baler twine, father got inside the trailer with the pig and slowly we began the return journey.

After a mile, both he and the pig began reversing out of the door, but he managed to hang on, and half a mile later he appeared to be riding her. We arrived back in one piece, with father's legs distinctly bowed. We will try again with a different trailer in ten days' time. Listen to the radio for reports of long tailbacks on the M25.

I had a strange phone call the other day. Somebody wanted to know whether the twist in a pig's tail is clockwise or anti-clockwise. The answer is 50 per cent appear to be clockwise and 50 per cent are

anti-clockwise. Perhaps a scientific study should be carried out to ascertain the reason why.

My vet has come up with an even stranger story – the other day he had a visit from a woman with a pet ferret suffering from a large abscess. Being a vegetarian, she had been trying to wean the animal off meat. Amazing – a carnivore not being allowed to eat its natural diet. It is rather like force-feeding a cow with pork sausages. I suppose then the cream would turn into pies instead of butter. It is becoming a strange world.

5

Kevin and Reynard

Society seems to have changed; when I was at the village junior school in the 1940s, whenever the hunt met in the parish we would all troop into the pub yard to see the hounds and horses. It was part of the autumn scene; many villagers lost hens to foxes each year and so the hunt was normal, natural and welcomed. We understood.

The hunt no longer comes to the village, as a motorway is too close for safety. Where it does meet it often gets a new breed of visitor, with paramilitary clothing, nose studs and dyed hair. Riders are insulted, spat at and even dragged from their horses. Unlike at football matches, the police usually just watch, as mainly urban incomers confront, disrupt and even terrorize. It is a countrywide story.

The troublemakers are hunt saboteurs. Hunt kennels have been set on fire, hunt houses have been daubed and even a non fox-hunting drag-hunt has been attacked (drag-hunts follow the scent of aniseed in a bag) showing the minuscule amount of knowledge possessed by some saboteurs. One master of hounds – a working farmer – even had her horses and cattle released onto the road at night, resulting in several animals being killed and injured. When an uninjured, unflustered stag appeared on a rooftop during a hunt a few years ago, headlines in the tabloid press screamed 'cruelty'. When the Master's favourite horse died with its head on her lap, the tabloid press was nowhere to be seen. Despite this, the police appear to have sided with the saboteurs, calling for hunting to be banned. They argue that the confrontation (which huntsmen do not seek) costs too much police time and money.

Society has changed; today urban values predominate, the individual freedom of rural people is at risk and local tradition and culture has no lasting place. Britain is being sanitized, homogenized,

13

and turned into a paradise for everything plastic and superficial. The imposition of urban and suburban values was taken a stage further with the introduction of a Bill into Parliament (the Second Reading of the Wild Mammals (Protection) Bill) that would ban hunting with hounds.*

But why should the anti-hunting movement worry me? I am simply a peasant farmer (a partner in 113 acres of heavy clay); I am an obsessive conservationist; I do not hunt, shoot or fish; I am not a member of the privileged classes; I did not go to public school, and I am not a member of the British Field Sports Society. The answer is simple; after much observation and consideration I do not regard hunting as cruel; hunting helps to conserve the natural habitat and hunting is part of my rural heritage and culture.

It is ironic, throughout the world there is concern for cultures threatened by the advance of 'civilization'. The pop singer Sting has

* Introduced by Kevin McNamara MP, February, 1992.

done much to publicize the plight of the rainforest Indians of Brazil
– he wants them to keep their hunting culture, against threats from
development and incomers uninterested in the old ways.

Yet in England, on Exmoor, another pop singer, Paul McCartney,
has bought land and forbidden the hunt to enter. It seems that he
is anxious to hasten the demise of old Exmoor as it retreats before
development, incomers and rich vegetarian pop singers.

Exmoor is an interesting case as its deer-hunting is almost universally reviled. Over 80 per cent of the population want deer-hunting
banned, and over 80 per cent of the population believe that the deer
are torn to pieces by hounds.

In fact the deer are not torn to pieces – they stand at bay and
are humanely shot. In other words, 80 per cent of the population
have made a judgement on things they simply do not understand
– often aided and abetted by dubious advertising. Some people call
this 'democracy'.

Exmoor is a unique place of heather-covered hills, isolated farms,
tree-lined combes, small villages and streams of clear water flowing
musically to the sea. It is not a wilderness, but a place of managed
wildness, where people have been linked closely to the land and
sea for generations. Shepherds, cattlemen, fishermen, farmers and
those who hunt Exmoor's deer have all been moulded by the moor
on which they live and work; they have traditions and a culture all
of their own.

It is part of their culture to hunt – not just to kill deer – but to
split up herds, so that deer damage is spread and shared, instead of
concentrated in a few places. Most of the people who live and work
on the moor support the hunt and love to see 'our deer'. Hunting
breaks the hard routine of moorland farming; it provides a social
life; it brings in income and it helps to preserve and to control
the deer.

Now, sadly, newcomers have been drawn by the lure of a
picture-postcard landscape. Often they are one-time holidaymakers
who have been attracted to stay for retirement; usually they arrive
from towns and bring their urban values with them. They know
best; they have seen the light and wish to legislate against the
'barbaric' country bumpkins around them.

They forget that Exmoor, its people and its wildlife need protection as an entity – just as much as other rural cultures in various
far-flung parts of the world. Communities all over Britain also
have close links with hunting – in the Cotswolds, the Lake
District, Leicestershire and many more. In all these places the
genuine countryman is under threat as the colonising urban hordes
advance.

Somewhere I read that not only should a democracy respond to the reasonable wishes of the majority, but it should also protect the rights and wishes of minorities. It seems that the indigenous countryman does not count as a minority in modern 'multi-cultural' Britain.

Much to the amazement of many, the anti-hunting Bill was defeated.

6

Foxes

I am beginning to wonder whether the birds and the bees can read, or watch television. Again this year, as soon as the shooting season ended, so the local pheasants appeared in droves, strolling about without a care in the world. Similarly, just as every urban eco-green in the country was heard praising the poor, misunderstood fox, as anti-hunting MPs tried (and failed) to get a Bill banning hunting through Parliament, so we had our first fox raid for months.

Inevitably our non-vegetarian, fur-wearing friend chose our most secure hen-house to break and enter. We bought the deep-litter shed when a local builder went bankrupt. No British worker would tolerate a tea-break in a draughty shed and so we thought the building would be ideal for our hens. The fox took great exception to this and ripped out a board, not to obtain a quiet snack, but to enjoy a banquet and create mayhem.

Thirteen hens bit the dust. One was taken into the orchard, where it was eaten, leaving just a heap of feathers; the rest were left where they dropped, or fluttered, in various stages of dismemberment. For us this loss was not just thirteen hens, but also dozens of eggs.

At one time the country fox was known as Reynard or Charlie; following Kevin McNamara MP's recent Bill, the locals round here have renamed the mischief-maker Kevin. I hope this particular Kevin has a conscience; it should realise that all this slaughter actually broke EC regulations and that by simply leaving the bodies it could also cause a salmonella threat, thus arousing the ire of Edwina Currie, a threat far more frightening for the fox than a pack of hounds.

A few years ago we would have given the corpses to friends. Now, because of the national neurosis about food, we will eat what the fox left ourselves – roast chicken, curried chicken and chicken pie, for the next fortnight. I hope the fox had cleaned its teeth.

From the signs and smells, Kevins come through the farmyard several times a week. Normally we leave them alone, but when trouble starts we have found that if we remove the troublemaker the problem is solved. The foxes with acceptable habits continue to visit but leave the hens alone.

We kill about one troublesome fox every three or four years. We set a free running snare at dusk and usually the fox is caught within two hours and shot humanely with a .22 rifle at close range. We always feel sad afterwards as foxes are beautiful animals, but we have no other options. Now, of course there are people who want to ban snares. If they succeed we will have to sit up all night with a rifle and hope that any ricochet or misdirected shot doesn't pot one of our neighbours or a passing container lorry.

Self-lock snares were rightly banned in 1981. There is a place however for the free running snare properly used. Then, if any unwanted animal is caught, it can usually be released quite easily. Strangely, in a recent RSPCA campaign to ban snaring, its picture of a snared deer seemed to me to show a self-lock snare, making the picture at least twelve years old. I phoned the RSPCA to ask the age of the picture and the type of snare depicted. Despite several inquiries, I received no answer. I wonder why?

Over the years I have had a number of foxes as pets. My last one, Rusty, came to me because she outgrew her owner's house and garden. She was a superb little vixen. Unlike dogs, foxes cannot be house-trained, and they are always nervous of strangers, but we soon became good friends. I kept her in a large run with a roof, as she was a good climber, and sunken wire, as she was an equally good digger. She would play with the dogs and I would take her for long walks on the lead, when she would pull the entire time. Anything that wandered through the wire into her run died quickly – usually hedgehogs, rats and blackbirds. She escaped several times, but always came back two or three days later.

Every day I would go into her run to stroke her and play with her. Often she would jump on to my shoulders and push her head through my hair. One day when she did this something was not quite right. Suddenly my hair felt wet and warm – she had relieved herself. Fox shampoos are not to be recommended: I could not get rid of the smell for days. I did not let her on my shoulders again.

Her end came in the spring of 1979 – election year. Following some sort of mental aberration I was standing as a Tory candidate in the Socialist Republic of Bethnal Green. It was then that Rusty decided to escape again, only this time she did not come back.

Several times I interrupted my 'campaign' to look for her – surely some sort of political record – and twice more campaigning was cancelled, to allow me to sneak home to play football; so at least some of my priorities remained sensible.

Eventually she was found dead, unmarked except for a broken neck. It was as if she had approached a large dog and had been chopped, dying instantly. So I lost a fox that I loved and regarded as a friend. I learned something however, as her death convinced me that a fox killed by a large dog faces a far quicker and more humane end than from a badly used gun, snare or cage. But at the time that was no great consolation.

7

Skating over the Past

Urban-dominated contemporary Britain is a strange place; whenever winter lives up to its seasonal reputation and delivers, snow, ice and a prolonged freeze, the country seizes up. Roads become chaotic. Trains stop. The news includes warnings of hypothermia, and the weather forecasters become almost apologetic, describing the thaw, when it comes, as 'good news'.

I am beginning to feel the odd man out, because I love cold winters. They are healthily invigorating; they give landscapes new beauty and, if warnings of the greenhouse effect are true, we might not have them for much longer. Whenever the freeze comes I put on gloves, an extra jumper and longjohns, and then while the rest of the country struggles to work, I am out in the fresh, clear air, ice skating. In fact, because of ice skating I actually hope, almost pray, for a cold winter.

My anticipation begins in October. On the morning of the first frost I find my skates in readiness for the winter wait. My cricket bat and tennis racket go to the back of the cupboard and the long steel blades of my speed skates are given pride of place. Speed skating, or fen skating, is a tradition in my part of Cambridgeshire, as it is in parts of Lincolnshire, Norfolk, Suffolk, Essex and various other areas where low land and high water tables mean shallow, still water that freezes quickly. Gliding along a river or over a flooded field is entirely different from skating on a boring indoor rink in figure skates.

I started skating almost as soon as I could walk. In those days water meadows had not been drained and ploughed to feed the European grain mountain. In summer they gave hay and housed grazing cattle; in winter they were empty, until the floods came. Then, after three nights of hard frosts, villagers would arrive to

skate, first testing the ice in the old way: 'If it cracks it bears; if it bends it breaks'. Some had fast, posh, racing skates, while others had to make do with blades screwed into the bottoms of old working boots, or 'fen-runners' – metal blades on a wooden base, strapped onto ordinary shoes.

My first attempt on the flooded meadows was at the age of three or four, with small fen-runners strapped to my boots. With a wooden chair in front of me for support, I would push off. At every fall my mother would pick me up and brush me down, and I would start again. The ice was crowded; my brother, sisters, parents, grandmother, aunts, uncles, cousins and various villagers were all skating too, round and round for hours. When the small brook froze we would skate on that too, weaving in and out of the rushes and under the archways of fallen willows.

Skating in moonlight was magical, with ice crystals reflecting the moonbeams, and lanterns marking bends and thin ice. On moonless nights car headlights provided illumination and Thermos flasks of hot soup gave inner warmth. My parents, and grandparents, too, had skated from a young age. My grandfather, born in 1872, learnt to skate with bullocks' ribs strapped to his boots. Whether he had the flat sides or the edges to the ice I have no idea. A great-uncle was also a keen skater and is said to have once skated from Cambridge to Ely on the frozen River Cam.

My grandmother skated until well into her eighties, although her last outing ended in disaster. She was told that she ought to give up, that she was too old and should not go alone. So, following a well-worn family trait, she ignored all advice, went alone, and fell heavily. She broke a wrist and, despite her pain, would not go to the doctor. She simply strapped it up and did not tell a soul or use her arm until it had healed.

The traditions of skating date back to before the seventeenth century. In the Fens, bone and wooden skates were used by fowlers and by those wanting to get about during frozen winters. Metal fen-runners followed, probably copied from skates brought over by Dutchmen involved in draining the land. The first recorded race took place in 1814, and races have been held in virtually every cold winter since.

Fewer people go skating now. One of the main reasons is that most of the country's water meadows have disappeared. Water authorities have drained rivers and sunk boreholes, lowering water tables so much that the traditional wet fields of winter no longer flood. In my father's childhood, fields were deliberately flooded at Lingey, close to where our brook flows into the Cam at Byron's Pool. Now those same fields are arable and are seldom submerged. It is a sad change and in my parish there is now nowhere to skate. Fortunately for us, the old tradition of flooding fields continues ten miles away at Earith, in the Fens. There a local farmer still floods the forty acres of Bury fen. Whenever frost is in the air he opens a 'slacker' (a sluice) which allows water from the Great Ouse to pour in. Once it has frozen, the thirty members of Over, Swavesey and Earith Skating Association, formed in 1913, measure a course and races are held, both local and national.

It is a fine sight; people enjoying themselves in the old ways – skating, sliding, falling – it is simple, unsophisticated sport, but exciting and extremely enjoyable. Old men still skate for hours, easily and rhythmically, their arms behind their backs, some with caps reversed to prevent them blowing off. Other sports have also hit the ice; ice hockey and sledges with sails and no brakes, that hurtle across the frozen water at speed.

My father, now in his late seventies, is contemplating retirement. Unfortunately, his skates have lost their edges and his boots are falling apart. When he and they were in their prime, he was a good skater; now he is unpredictable. Last time out, his legs went from under him and those skaters following close behind toppled over his sprawling form like ninepins – it was spectacular.

But I keep on skating, sometimes followed by Bramble, my dog, for travelling at speed, outside, over ice, gives a tremendous sense of freedom – of both movement and spirit. It is a combination of easy movement, the sound of metal on ice; the cold wind on cheeks; the glare of sun on frozen water; the gentle light of the moon on new snow; arctic swans and widgeon passing overhead – it is a way of feeling close to nature in an increasingly unnatural world.

Unfortunately, the future of traditional fen skating is not assured. Last year, for the first time in living memory, the course for the skating championships, carefully marked out by volunteers, was smashed up by hooligans the night before the races, causing them to be cancelled. In addition, some newcomers to the Fens cannot skate, or understand local traditions. After a small boy got wet feet in the 18 inches of water below the ice, his mother phoned the police to complain about the 'danger'. Constable Plod reluctantly arrived and the farmer had to put Danger signs on his gate.

For more than 100 years people have been skating at Bury fen. Now the suburban ice-breakers and the police-complainers have moved in. Yet another country tradition is under threat from people who simply do not understand.

8

Starlings and Red Legs

At this time of year I love the dusk, for I can set my watch by the huge flocks of starlings that fly over the farm. They fly over almost exactly half an hour before sunset and I expect this to continue until well into March. On damp, overcast days they will come a few minutes early, but on a fine evening it is possible to set your watch by them. They do not arrive in tens, hundreds or even thousands, but in hundreds of thousands, looking like a huge swarm of bees, or locusts. I am glad the farm seems to have become a beacon on their flight path.

In the wind they come by low, hedge-hopping, but on fine evenings they will pass directly over us, with the only noise being the collective whisper of their wings. Even the cattle in the yard stop mooing for their food to look upwards with bucolic interest. Usually there will be a number of large flocks, one after the other, but sometimes they will merge into a huge single flock.

Occasionally they have a change of plan and instead of passing over the farm, they fall out of the sky to roost; all the trees and telephone wires around become a black murmuring mass. Wave after wave will come in with the edges of each flock flowing and changing in regular, rounded shapes; the movement of bodies and wings in the air hold the same symmetry as oil on water. Then, without warning, they will be off, flying towards the sunset and their roost.

It will happen most years, until suddenly they stop coming, or their flight path changes. Old Charlie used to have the answer: 'They'll stay in their roost until they stink themselves out, and then they'll find somewhere else until it gets sweeter again.' There must be at least three quarters of a million birds some evenings and when they land the noise of their conversations is enormous;

it sounds as if they are all trying to discuss the day's activities at the same time.

At one time I disliked starlings, for being brash and greedy, but I have since come to enjoy their company. In the country they can do much good work by removing tons of harmful 'leatherjackets' and wireworms from the soil. It is astonishing that just 150 years ago one of the 'common' names for the starling was 'the solitary thrush', because it was so uncommon. At that time too some people regarded the grey/brown immature birds as a different species – a type of migrating thrush – that left us in the winter. In fact millions of continental birds join us in the winter because of our milder climate.

Starlings can be good mimics. We have one that regularly visits the cattleyard and wolfwhistles; I get caught out nearly every time, looking up to see which local beauty is walking by. A few years ago we had one that would copy my father whistling his wayward border collie and we have had a variety of duck, pheasant and mynah bird impressionists.

One of the first signs of spring is when their black winter beaks turn to bright yellow. Already out of all the thousands of birds that visit us, we have spotted one with a bright yellow beak.

In the summer sun their plumage is astonishing. It was best described by the late Kenneth Allsop: 'What exotic rarity was this which had settled on the barn ridge tiles? What fantastic jungle fowl had strayed from the tropics into my damp valley? Actually, nothing to send an earthquake through the ornithological world. It was just a common or garden starling, singing its common or garden serenade, which has the melodious euphony of a two-stroke engine blowing a gasket.'

My father enjoys the starlings too, but he gets even more pleasure from miseducating the ignorant. The other day as the flocks came over, a visitor asked: 'What are those birds?'

'Starlings', my father replied.

'Really? I thought they went away in winter. Where do they all come from?'

'Russia.'

'How do you know they're Russian?'

'Because they've all got red legs.'

'Well, I never knew that before.'

Neither did I.

No, I am not going mad; I was looking through some old diaries the other day and found this one, only four years old. Since then the number of starlings has plummeted. What has happened to them? Where have they gone? Or has some disaster struck? If numbers continue to fall then the starling could soon become known as the 'solitary thrush' again.

9

A Walk on the Warmed Side

It is said that any great, or exciting, journey should never be attempted twice. The repeat can never match the original experience, it is like an action-replay – predictable, second hand and slightly unreal. Having just plodded up to Uhuru Peak for the second time – the 19,340 ft summit of Mount Kilimanjaro, Africa's highest mountain – I disagree. What a masochistic way to spend a few winter days away from our small low lying farm!

For years the mountain has fascinated and almost haunted me; I saw it first many years ago in pictures, films and books; suddenly, from the parched, hot, dusty plains of Kenya and Tanzania there it was, a huge dome of equatorial, arctic Africa. At just 190 miles south of the Equator, beyond plains teeming with gazelles, antelopes and lurking carnivores, was an elevated frozen world of glaciers, crevasses and cliffs of ice. It was incredible; almost unbelievable.

Way back in 1849 it was considered to be totally unbelievable. When Johann Rebmann, a missionary for the London based Church Missionary Society, first reported a huge snow-capped mountain to the Royal Geographical Society, he was greeted with derision – almost as a geo-terrorist, a non-geographer hallucinating or seeing mirages and reporting things he simply did not understand. Soon however, it became clear that Johann Rebmann was not dreaming, the 'experts' were wrong, Kilimanjaro did exist and men froze on it and died on it before its icy wastes were finally conquered in 1889, by the German explorer Hans Meyer.

I first saw the actual mountain in 1979 on a journey south; suddenly Kilimanjaro was almost the entire landscape, rising huge and white-topped out of Negley Farson's 'miles and miles and miles of Sweet Fanny Adams'. Since then, as I have explored Africa the easy twentieth-century way, the mountain has often been in the background, just beyond Tsavo, the Athi Plains, the Shimba Hills, the Chuli Hills and Lake Jipe. It is a beautiful, majestic mountain – a huge old volcano, named from its Kiswahili root of *kilima* (small hill) – showing either affection, distortion or a highly developed sense of humour.

But was I seeing the same mountain as Johann Rebmann and Hans Meyer? At times Kilimanjaro seemed to be covered by snow, but at others it appeared to be almost bare; certainly not the wasteland of snow and ice experienced by those early missionaries, travellers and pioneers.

In 1989, one hundred years after the first climb, I decided to try the ascent myself, setting off from the famous Marangu Hotel, near Moshi, the traditional starting point. As a middle-aged, overweight, undergrown asthmatic, I was not a pretty sight. Yet after three tiring days I managed to wheeze my way to the top, drug-assisted, with generous doses of Ventolin, Becotide, aspirin, paracetamol, Kendal mint cake (if that is a drug) and Diamox – yes Diamox – a drug used to combat pre-menstrual tension. Now pre-menstrual tension has never been one of my problems, but Diamox has also been found to ward off the effects of altitude sickness – cerebral oedema and pulmonary oedema, both of which in mild forms can send people off the mountain defeated, while in extreme forms they can have their victims carried off dead.

The climb was exhausting; I felt ill, but at the same time euphoric, as natural adrenalin mixed with the unnatural drug cocktail to help me onward and upward. But was I hallucinating? Where was the snow? Once at the bottom again all I had were mental images of bare rock and cinders, seen through a haze of high altitude elation. I decided that I had to take a second look, only next time more properly prepared mentally, and physically.

In fact my recent climb was not an action replay as it was attempted from the Kenyan side of the mountain. The journey to the foothills of Kilimanjaro was through Masailand in drought, to the dusty border town of Loitokitok and its Outward Bound School, established in 1952. There, two exceptional Kikuyu instructors, Chris Kibuku and Naftaly Ng'ang'a, plus an army of porters, were preparing to take me, with Mike Fitzgerald, an ex-BBC producer, Anthony Cheffings, a partner in Bateleur Safaris, Patrick Musyoka the Bateleur cook, and five assorted Americans, to the top of the mountain. The Americans made an interesting collection – one dressed like a liberated Karen Blixen in a long skirt, straw hat and no bra – she was already Blixenating – two women fitted out in baseball caps, and an older couple, Bill and Bertha, dressed as if visiting the Davey Crockett memorial. Had nobody told them that they were about to attempt a 'serious mountain' on which people could die? Suspiciously there were two absentees; the American organizer who had decided that an elk shoot in Colorado was more appealing than half oxygen at 19, 000 feet, and the Kenyan organizer, who suddenly found tennis and sundowners in one of Nairobi's gin and tonic suburbs a far better bet than hyperventilating at −10°C.

The aim was to spend four days walking up the mountain – one day longer than usual, to allow for better altitude acclimatization, and one and a half days down. Incredibly, in 1959 an English instructor at Loitokitok, Ralph Clough, now living in Scotland, made the complete journey in 14 hours 55 minutes, to win a place in the Guinness Book of Records.

Once past the Tanzanian 'border post' (a rather grand description for something that resembled a free-range chicken shed) we were set down on a woodland path. Bill and Bertha seemed bemused; almost as if they had expected a cable car to the top – alas for them they were at least twenty years too early.

Equatorial rain forest has an aura quite unlike anything else, with tall trees, the smell of decaying leaves, creepers, and birds and butterflies searching for sunlight high above. As we walked we passed from one musical territory of birdsong to the next, along a narrow winding track taking us ever upward.

Gradually forest gave way to bracken and conifers, and rain came. Bill and Bertha plodded on, already sounding defeated – not an unknown feeling for a former pilot who had seen action in Korea and Vietnam.

The rain fell heavier and we were offered a choice of cave or tent. Bill and Bertha chose the damp, cramped luxury they knew, a tent; I chose the cave. I had never slept in a cave before. It was a strangely relaxing experience – the oldest form of shelter in Africa and one in which primitive nomadic people once sought security. It was easy to see why early Bushmen had once painted in caves, for as the firelight sent shadows dancing in and over the uneven roof, the flickering light would have given life to their ancient art.

Dawn came cold, clear and damp. Patrick cooked porridge over an open fire; his plan was to provide good, simple food, containing plenty of protein and carbohydrate. On my previous trip the menu had not been well thought out; the sequence had been hot chicken, warm chicken, cold chicken and neat salmonella.

The secret of beating altitude sickness, apart from taking Diamox, is to drink as much water as possible and conserve energy by walking slowly. I found the idea of walking slowly very appealing, and as BBC Mike and Karen Blixen charged off into the distance with the porters, I walked at a pace that made an amble seem exhausting

– just keeping in contact with Bill and Bertha. Where we moved onto moorland, with high heather and shrubs, a gorge had stunted pines draped in long swathes of lichen. Then came short heather and scrub, with patches of wind-dried flowers that would have fetched a fortune in Surbiton.

We climbed well above the clouds and the air seemed thin. Breathing became more laboured, and in the evening, even Bill and Bertha settled into a cave. It was like a major move for them; the only thing missing was the Pickford's lorry.

Night in remote Africa is a very special time. In the developed West, with our urbanization and homogenization, we have lost the appreciation of real darkness and the silence that goes with it. There, 13,500 feet up the mountain we had darkness; a still, quiet darkness – night as night should be, with the stars appearing clearer and nearer because of the altitude.

Americans seem to have the gift to ruin any mood. Bill saw a small striped mouse: 'It's a chipmunk', he informed us. Then: 'I could do with a douche.' 'A what?', I queried, not being fluent in American. 'A shower – the English call it a douche, at least the women do.' Of course, I should have known. Clearly Bill was a fount of all wisdom. Earlier near Amboseli he had seen a Masai goat: 'In the United States', he informed us, 'we call that a goat – what do you call it?' On seeing a bare-breasted Masai woman he was even more revealing. 'Is that a woman?', he asked. In view of Bertha's liberal use of make-up and her designer, African Queen, safari suit, it was easy to understand his confusion.

After the first day we saw no more rain; it was so much drier than the Merangu side, with fewer trees and no giant groundsel or lobelias. The lack of streams meant the porters had to haul water quite long distances, for the higher we reached the drier it became. On the fourth day we were travelling over high altitude desert – bare rock, lava and cinders. Astonishingly, at 14,800 ft we crossed a trail left by eland and buffalo; apparently they climb to over 18,000 ft to reach small caves that have become salt licks.

By the early afternoon we had crossed 'the Saddle' and reached Kibo Hut, (over 15,400 ft), at the base of the crater – ready for the hardest and final climb. As usual Chris and Ng'an'a took us several hundred feet higher, before returning to the hut, their motto being 'climb high, sleep low' – a natural way of combating altitude sickness.

There is a need for a hut at Kibo, as the weather can be severe, but there is no need for the squalor that surrounds it. Supposedly in a 'wilderness area', it is gradually turning into a rubbish tip, as tin cans and assorted junk are carried up the mountain, but not carried down.

At midnight we woke up for the final climb, from Kibo Hut to the crater rim at Gillman's Point – a climb of over 3,000 feet, across a horizontal distance of just over 3,000 yards. In other words it is a very steep climb, and in half oxygen it can be agonizing. By now we all wore our cold weather clothes and even Karen Blixen had turned to trousers and a bra. Patrick too had been dragged away from his cooking fire and equipped with jumpers, coats and longjohns. Bertha was the only one who could go no further; she stayed in bed with a migraine or, more likely, mild altitude sickness.

As we trudged off it was surprisingly warm and my adrenalin was already flowing. Chris and Ng'ang'a had us walking 'pole, pole' – slowly, slowly – past the grave of a German who had keeled over with altitude sickness several years before. 'Slowly, slowly', we zig-zagged up the scree, Bill gasping – 'Alright Bill?' 'Can't talk, can't talk.'

Higher and harder; Karen Blixen and BBC Mike began to wilt, Mike having to stop frequently in order to hyperventilate. He sounded like a cross between a dying duck and a rutting rhino. Surprisingly, my normally suspect lungs, that on a visit to London are quickly reduced to wheezing, were clear and good, and although the American women claimed to be 'freezing', I still did not find it cold enough for gloves; evidently years of milking the farmhouse cow on freezing February mornings is good training for high altitude cold.

After 5½ hours we had nearly all made the crater rim at Gillman's Point, with Mike gasping, Anthony looking close to death and Karen Blixen unable to carry on. Even Bill, at sixty-two, arrived three hours later, each step being encouraged by Ng'ang'a. Then it was on to Uhuru Peak – another 500 feet up, and over one and a quarter miles along the rim; the cold even forced me to put on my gloves. The scree and cinders were easy; but with the lack of oxygen, scrambling over rocks turned into agony; I wanted to be sick, I wanted to relieve myself, I wanted to die – all at the same time. If anybody had offered me membership of 'Exit' I would have accepted. But despite the discomfort we made it – 19,340 feet. Twenty-six year old Anthony Cheffings, tough and extrovert, with normally moderate language, looked ill. 'I feel like a great big bag of . . .', he informed us – appearances were not deceptive.

Briefly I felt good and alert. Yes, to the south there was a glacier, with spectacular icicles and 40 ft cliffs of solid ice, but the crater itself was almost empty of snow. From pictures of a snow covered wilderness just fifty years ago the snow and ice had almost gone, and even as we stood at the edge of the southern glacier another large chunk of melting ice crashed down. Ng'ang'a had noticed a difference in just the four years he had been climbing the mountain. Joe Cheffings, father of Anthony, a well known and respected Kenyan conservationist, first climbed to Gillman's Point through deep snow and ice twenty five years ago. When he returned to the same spot in 1989 without touching ice, he was shocked: 'Until then I did not believe in global warming. Now I've seen it – it's frightening.' Ian Edwards of the Wilderness Trust first flew over the mountain in the early seventies and between 1983 and 1989 he flew regularly from Nairobi to Moshi to buy coffee. He too has been alarmed by what he has seen: 'The snow has become considerably less over the years. I am being totally unscientific, but there is no doubt about it, the retreat of snow and ice has been dramatic.'

Sitting on top of Kilimanjaro and looking across Africa provides another shock, for it is possible to look over hundreds of square miles of earth and realize just how thin the life-supporting atmosphere around the planet actually is. As I sat on top of Uhuru Peak, I was already above most of the world's oxygen – I could see its depth, yet into this thin layer we are pouring billions of tons of pollution and the atmosphere is changing. It seemed remarkable, almost suicidal; all those people miles away, driving to Tescos and sitting in their shirtsleeves in front of their television sets on a cold November day, actually helping to melt the snows of Kilimanjaro with their pollution.

So instead of being an almost arctic experience, Kilimanjaro is becoming a mountain of exposed ash; it is the place to go to see global warming in action. But just as Johann Rebmann was thought by some to be a geographical illiterate when he first reported seeing a snow-capped mountain in Africa, so today there are still scientists and politicians who refuse to believe in global warming, despite the obvious fact that within the not too distant future Kilimanjaro will be snowless.

One politician, Teresa Gorman is even reported to have called those who warn of global warming 'eco-terrorists'. Perhaps she should try to climb Kilimanjaro to see for herself. Such an achievement would also have one other obvious advantage – at half oxygen it would induce her to talk rather less.

10

Robbing Paul to Pay Pierre

A grain merchant called at the farm the other day desperately seeking 'feed wheat' (wheat to feed farmstock); he was offering £140 per ton, a price unheard of for several years. Unfortunately, we had sold all our wheat for far less straight after harvest.

'Get it from the grain mountain', I suggested. 'What grain mountain?' he replied. 'The one the politicians keep telling us about,' I went on innocently, as I always believe politicians. The grain merchant was not impressed: 'The grain mountain disappeared months ago.'

So, as usual I phoned the Ministry of Agriculture: 'Why is wheat £140 a ton?' I inquired. A sweet, well-rehearsed voice immediately replied on autodrive: 'It's because of the CAP, the system that pays farmers to produce too much grain . . .'

Quite out of character, I interrupted: 'That's wrong – the price is far higher than usual and it is higher because the British grain mountain has disappeared'.

Silence followed, then: 'That doesn't make sense, does it? I'll go to the policy division.' A few minutes later she phoned back. It was official, from the policy division: we have no grain mountain.

Then I phoned the Intervention Board – the quango that buys surplus grain and so physically creates grain mountains. It confirmed that the British mountain has vanished – just 34,000 tons of feed wheat and 495 tons of bread wheat remain – creating a mole-hill. Britain is out of wheat.

'But why do the politicians keep telling us that British farmers have created grain mountains?' I asked. 'I don't know,' the official replied, 'we don't get involved with this.' In fact Britain is now importing wheat from France, at the same time as the Government is taking land out of cereal production. The British taxpayer is having to pay British farmers to grow nothing on 'set-aside' land, while the British housewife is paying French farmers for cereals that the British farmer is no longer growing. What a wonderful system. I wonder if British car manufacturers will ever be asked to stop making cars, to allow in more French vehicles? Of course not. Can we have an explanation please, Mr Gummer?

I have some good news. Snowdrop is pregnant. Eventually we managed to get her to Buckinghamshire, via the M25, where she met a very charming boar called 'Sladepark Raja', or 'Jacko' to his friends. My father did not make the journey on this occasion as he did not want to end up in the trailer with the pig again.

The reason for the success of this journey was a borrowed trailer. It was an excellent trailer, rather like a padded cell on wheels, made in Wales. It struck me that such a secure and well made Welsh trailer could have another use – ferrying Neil Kinnock inconspicuously between his constituency and Parliament – only to ensure his own comfort and privacy of course. If he would like a trial run we could pick him up on our return trip to retrieve Snowdrop, although of course, it would be rather unfair on the pig.

In these days of declining farm incomes all losses are unwelcome, whether caused by visits from foxes, machinery breaking down, falling prices, or simply bad luck. We have just had some bad luck – a whole field of oats has been killed by frost. We always grow oats; they do well on our soil and the straw can be fed to cattle. Some oats we grind up and feed to our animals, and some we sell. Strangely the market can never be predicted; one year a porridge oats manufacturer took them virtually straight off the field, but at other times they can hang about for months. Sadly, after next harvest we will have no winter oats to sell at all, as the whole field is brown, lifeless and dead. Yet the germination was good and by the end of October it looked as green as a lawn. One villager actually stopped me in the Post Office: 'I went for a walk the other day, Robin – that's a good field of oats you've got this year.' He's quite a knowledgeable old boy, shown by the fact that not many people can tell the difference between two inch high wheat, barley and oats. But in farming you should never count your chickens before they hatch – or weigh your corn before it is harvested; the hard frosts of December somehow froze and lifted the surface of the soil, snapping the young plants just below the ground. Virtually the whole crop has been killed. Now we will have to plant a fresh crop of spring oats or barley in March or April, depending on the weather; it is a reminder too of just how dependent farming is, and always will be, on the weather; it should also be seen as a warning. To some politicians food surpluses are a great evil; but what happens in the future if there is a widespread crop failure due to the vagaries of the weather and all the food mountains have gone? The answer is simple, there will be a lot of food for thought, but not too much to eat.

11

Veggie-Burghers

For those of us who live in the country, entertainment can be hard to come by during the winter. Television is usually boring and my old Roberts radio cannot cope with some strange system called FM, or something like that. So, whenever I want to be entertained I turn to the written word and search out the latest pontifications of the Secretary of State for Agriculture, John Selwyn Gummer. Well, he was John Selwyn Gummer once; somewhere along the line he appears to have lost the Selwyn – in much the same way that Tony Benn has lost the Anthony and the Wedgwood. Who knows, with an election coming up, perhaps John Worzel Gummidge could even become Johnny Gum, in an effort to identify with the common man. 'Vote for Johnny Gum', it sounds just right for a classless society.

Well, Johnny Gum has just announced a campaign to counteract the advance of vegetarianism. He is particularly worried about young veggie girls; it is strange how high churchmen often seem to take an extremely close interest in young girls. I have even heard a story of a vicar who once took a very close interest in the organist – behind the organ.

Anyway, John Gummer is worried about calories and vitamins and things like that; apparently young girls are simply not getting enough of what does them good these days, because of a diet of soya milk, nut cutlets and bean sprouts. Now he wants to blast them with reason in the hope that they will all soon be eating beefburgers and hot dogs again. How anybody could be attracted to this disgusting American food is beyond me; he should be persuading them to eat meat puddings, tripe and onions and bread and dripping – delicious.

But surely he also ought to be trying to terrify these poor waifs and strays into seeing sense. What I would do if I was Johnny Gum would be to run a poster campaign – it would feature a large picture of Linda McCartney, followed by a Government Health Warning and 'If you become a Vegetarian – you too could look like this woman.' I believe that all teenage girls worried about their faces and figures would become carnivores immediately.

But why does Linda McCartney look as she does? She might be a very pleasant lady, but to me she always looks intense and worried. If I were a vegetarian I would look intense and worried too; according to one of the last programmes I managed to pick up on my radio, soya beans, the staple diet of affluent Western veggies, come from India and Brazil. In India the desire to export soya has turned a healthy and renewable form of agriculture into a non-renewable system of factory farming, growing a cash crop. It is soya monoculture, made possible by imported chemicals and fertilizers and leading to the destruction of a fragile soil structure. In Brazil, so it is said, soya beans are being grown on ground cleared of rain forest. Some of these vegetarians have a lot to answer for; so well done Johnny Gum.

I have another complaint about vegetarians: it is a medical fact, according to one expert, that they pass wind more often than those of us on a mixed diet. As a direct result it is the methane produced by vegetarians that is currently still attacking the ozone layer, so it is said. Is this true or is it not, Linda McCartney? We need to know the answer.

To all those people awash with water in the North West of Britain, the following story will be of no interest whatsoever – in the South East of England there is a drought. The reason for this is simple; nearly all the engineers of the National Rivers Authority have not been taught about rivers, so it appears, instead they have been taught how to 'drain'. Consequently if they see a puddle, pond or drop of dew, the immediate reaction is 'drain it' – drain, drain drain. So thanks to assorted pasty-faced young water engineers nearly all our rivers, streams, brooks and ditches have been turned into efficient drains, and water can no longer be held back. As a result, whenever it rains all the water rushes straight off the land and away. Consequently there are water engineers today who are actually being paid large salaries to produce water shortages – incredible.

Years ago, during a drought, the advice would be to put a brick in your cistern, have a bath with a friend and only wash your hair once a week (as often as that?) to save water. With water privatization however, the water companies want us to use all the water, and all the water-using gadgets, as much as possible, 'for the benefit of our shareholders'. Why should they worry themselves about little things such as rivers and lakes drying up and East Anglia turning into a semi-desert? The National Rivers Authority is supposed to be the 'watchdog' to prevent over-use; sadly in reality it is the 'sleeping dog', or even the 'dead dog'.

Nearly all the water officials I have ever met have looked extremely seedy – I think it must be through working in air-conditioned offices. One had a terrible problem; he did not need 'Head and Shoulders' (an anti-dandruff shampoo), he needed Head, Shoulders, Front, Back and Both Sides. I am told that this condition is known today as dry scalp; out here we call it 'scurf'. It's sad how all the words that we grew up with are gradually disappearing as time marches on – feet, inches, gallons, fundament and scurf, to name just a few.

Living near Cambridge we have several intellectuals who visit the local pub who tell jokes that I don't understand. E.g. 'What does DNA stand for?'

'National Association of Dyslexics.' I'm comtlepely daffleb.

12

A Dog's Life

If there is such a thing as reincarnation, then I want to come back again as a dog. I like dogs and ours have good lives, like most farm dogs. My little lurcher Bramble has the best position in front of the fire during the winter and his summer days are occupied by eating, sleeping and chasing the bull, with occasional bouts of freelance rabbiting or ratting thrown in for good measure. The main danger of a reprimand comes from chasing cats and even then it depends on which cat is being chased.

In my simple, rustic view, Man's relationship with dogs is not based on dominance or sentiment, but on companionship and mutual respect, for a dog really is a 'man's best friend'. Inevitably these days there are some pseudo-intellectual urban weirdos who maintain that close affection for a dog is a sign of a major personality deficiency. If that is the case then I am extremely happy being deficient. Indeed one of the great pleasures in life must be to sleep in front of a great log fire surrounded by dogs, rather like the old squire in Henry Fielding's *Tom Jones*. At one time it must have been quite a common practice, hence the old saying:

> He that lieth down with the dogs,
> Shall rise up with fleas.

At one time we had five dogs on the farm. The oldest was Tyra, given a Swedish name by my Swedish sister-in-law. She was a fine old dog and I will always remember her with affection. She was born when I was living as a 'down and out'; dossing, to see if the old romantic tramp was still wandering the highways and byways – he was not. I was feeling depressed, cold and hungry, having left an old style Reception Centre at Brighton to walk to Eastbourne in a day, via the Seven Sisters and Beachy Head. At a small hamlet I phoned home to report my whereabouts, to be told that our faithful old dog Tinker had given birth to her first litter. The whole litter consisted of one fat female puppy, Tyra. Her greatest achievement during a life of leisure and contentment was to let a builder into a shed to collect a bag of cement, only to refuse to let him out again, with snarls and her teeth bared.

The other dog who has left for the great box of Bonios in the sky was a border collie called Ben. Like most 'sheep dogs' he was highly strung and never happier than when hooves were flying and he was trying to hang onto the tail of a straying or straggling cow. He came to us after being rescued by a vet from a bad city home. With one ear up and one ear down, it was thought that he had been mistreated – swung by the neck while on a choke chain and beaten.

Because of this we tried to give him a good home; but even after years of kindness he always growled and snapped when put on his chain at night. His party piece was car tyres. Shortly after his arrival several visitors found themselves with punctures, two or three hundred yards from the farm; a commercial traveller claimed that Ben was the culprit. We laughed; how could a dog puncture a modern car tyre? The answer came quite soon afterwards and was 'very easily indeed'. A man called at the farm for eggs. As soon as the car stopped Ben attacked one of the front tyres; there was an ominous hissing sound and Ben looked pleased. His career total went well into double figures, in spite of our efforts to teach him of the wonders of pneumatic travel.

Now, the three remaining dogs are Husky, Rinty and Bramble. Rinty is a labrador with a blood-curdling deep bark. It is just what is required on a farm when roving scrap-dealers call. His fixation is not tyres but water, or more accurately anything that he thinks is liquid, such as pond, puddle or cowpat. Whatever it is he will flop into it, and then shake himself over the nearest observer. During the winter he will swim from one icy bank of the brook to the other, and in the summer he is rarely dry. He does not simply jump into water – he launches himself, with feet spread out for maximum splash.

During one hot summer when Ben was still biting tyres they wandered off together into one of the newish estates in the village. Much to Rinty's joy they came across a small ornamental fish pond. Both dogs leapt in, thankful for such consideration.

Bramble is a lurcher; the first one that I have owned and, hope-fully, not the last. Although the Kennel Club does not recognize the lurcher as a breed, who needs the Kennel Club when you have a lack of pedigree to match Bramble's? He was bred by Monty Christopher, the retired ex-headkeeper to the Queen at Sandringham. He wanted

to breed something that would look like a miniature wolfhound. By introducing a friend's short-haired whippet lurcher to a pedigree Argentinian Bedlington terrier, he succeeded, and Bramble resulted. The first day I had him the local gypsy was so impressed that he offered me £25.

In his habits Bramble is dainty, almost foxlike; but strangely the one animal that he cannot abide is the fox – a dislike shared by all the other dogs we have ever had, except when we have had tame foxes. The first animal he ever chased was a fox and he seems to remember the place where each incident occurs, as if an action replay is certain to follow. The lurcher of tradition hunts with his eyes and chases in silence; the Bramble of reality uses his nose as often as his eyes and when he chases he yaps in high-pitched excitement.

An example of his keen sense of smell occurred one Sunday afternoon, again in the reign of Ben. Rinty and Ben had continued keenly along the brook bank, but Bramble stopped by an old pollarded willow. He looked up quizzically, smelling the air, before standing up on his back legs and sniffing up into the branches. I assumed that he had located an early mallard sitting on eggs and went to check the tree. As I gripped a crack in the hollow trunk, to climb, I had a shock; for as my hand went in, a fox looked out. The other two dogs returned and bedlam broke out. The fox with his usual exit blocked, jumped, from a height of ten feet, to perform a spectacular belly flop into the brook. It was the first time I had seen a fox swim. Rinty and Ben piled in after it, while Bramble, who hates water, thought momentarily. The fox was away, so he jumped, clearing the water completely, yapping hysterically as he quickly overtook the other dogs. As soon as the fox reached a ditch and a hedge, the unorthodox hunt was over. The dogs were baffled, sniffing around, with their heads down; the fox had simply disppeared into thin air.

Now every time we pass the willow Bramble still pauses and looks upwards. He should know better – for 'A fox is not taken twice in the same snare.'

13

Selection for an Election

It is official, the countryside is unfit for human habitation, at least according to a Labour Party worker. My nephew Andrew works on a large farm in Yorkshire. His farm cottage is in a small hamlet well off the beaten track – just what he wanted. Shortly before the election a representative for the local Labour Candidate called; the poor man's urban mind was appalled: 'If we get elected', he promised, 'I will get you street lights and pavements. You need more houses too, and what about the local children? All they have to do is watch television.' In other words he promised Andrew and his wife everything they do not want.

In fact the local children have a wonderful time; they have woods, grass fields and water meadows, where they can enjoy traditional country childhoods. They may not know the difference between a Ford Sierra and a Honda Accord, but they can catch sticklebacks and recognize the song of the skylark. The sad truth is that most urban politicians do not understand the countryside or the genuine country people who live in it.

America has reservations for its Indians; Australia has reservations for its Aborigines – when are English rustics who don't want street lights, motorways, junk food and light-weight urban politicians, going to get reservations here? If ever a reservation is created, I will be the first in; I suspect my father will be the second, closely followed by Worzel Gummidge. The reservation would pay for itself easily – bus loads of gawping urbanites could drive through for a fee, with a hurdlemaker, wheelwright, thatcher, blacksmith, wood-turner and potter to stare at. It is right that such craftsmen should be in a reservation, as they are all endangered species and gradually disappearing as the hi-tech, plastic revolution takes over.

Mention of natives reminds me of an absurd injunction from the Countryside Commission that there must be no staring at coloured people in the countryside. Apparently this displays prejudice and racism; what is more the Countryside Commission wants to see black people building dry stone walls, hedgelaying and sheep shearing.

Now if I saw a black, brown, yellow or green person building a dry stone wall in the middle of Dartmoor, not only would I stare, but I would also take a photograph. When I go to Africa, I am frequently stared at by black people. In the rain forest of Zaire, not only was I stared at, but as I approached, the local children shouted in their language: 'White man, white man.' I did not regard it as racism, but as healthy, friendly interest. If I had stopped to make a dugout canoe, I would have expected them to stare even harder.

Several years ago I saw American Peace Corps volunteers dressed up as Swazi warriors at the Coronation of King Mswati 3rd; they looked patronizing and absurd. To me, black people building dry stone walls or Morris dancing would look equally absurd – sorry.

If the Countryside Commission is really anxious to stop prejudice why doesn't it look closer to home? When we had a dairy herd a few years ago people would frequently wind down their car windows as we drove the cows along the road, to say such intelligent things as 'Ooh ahhh, hallo Phil Archer, is it milking time, ooh ahhh, ooh ahhh', accompanied by screams of near hysterical laughter from the other occupants. Even now some friends of another nephew greet me with such things as: 'Ooh ahhh, ooh ahhh Farmer Robin – I must go and do my sheep shearing ooh ahhh'. This isn't racism, but peasantism, and what does the Countryside Commission intend to do about it? And when is the Countryside Commission, or the race relations industry going to force the BBC to have newsreaders with broad rural Devonshire, Norfolk, Oxfordshire or Cambridgeshire accents?

At the moment the subject of prejudice seems to be the subject of much prejudice.

A neighbouring farmer pointed out something extremely interesting the other day – how all the hysteria about listeria and salmonella has suddenly died down. With an election approaching the politicians are now talking about what they regard as the real issues; as a result all the phoney food scares have dropped well into the background. Ever since Edwina Currie MP induced anti-egg hysteria and obtained maximum publicity, my neighbour believes that raising food scares has become a political device to boost flagging political reputations. He is convinced that in a future political lull, somebody of Mrs Currie's ilk will point out that natural manure is unhygienic: 'Muck heaps will become illegal,' he says, 'cows and pigs will have to wear nappies and organic food grown with manure will be banned as "unfit for human consumption".'

I had a phone call the other day from a young lady working for her PhD. I was astonished, it was actually a sensible PhD; she was studying the impact of set-aside on wildlife. What was even more astonishing however, was the behaviour of the Ministry of Agriculture. The Ministry is funding the graduate's study, but it has refused to give her a list of those farmers who have taken the set-aside option; so how can she study her subject? Someone at the Ministry should be given an honorary PhD in Bureacratic Art, Craft and Incompetence.

Last week I came across a Ministry set-aside official pushing a measuring wheel in the middle of one of our fields. She was checking to make sure that we had not ploughed up any of our set-aside. During this economic recession I hope that measuring wheel manufacturers are aware of their great business opportunities.

14

Rooks – as the Crow Flies

I never thought the time would arrive when I would miss rooks and jackdaws, but it has. During my childhood they vied with sparrows for the position of most numerous birds in the village. At some time or other most village boys had a pet jackdaw, almost always called, with amazing originality, 'Jack'.

The jackdaws have gone because they have nowhere to nest. There are just no old trees with suitable holes for nesting sites in the southern part of the parish and some of the suburban minded new villagers would never allow jackdaws to build in their chimneys as a substitute. A few birds remain in some skeletal elms in the northern part of the parish and the occasional group passes over in winter, but sadly the jackdaw has virtually passed out of my life.

The rooks are still more numerous, but they too now find things difficult. Several years ago at this time of year I could count the nests in a nearby rookery from my study window and I loved to hear their calls coming in on the wind. The rookery disappeared with the arrival of Dutch Elm Disease; the trees fell down or were chopped down and the rooks had to look elsewhere for places to nest. In a landscape dominated by the elm and ravaged by prairie farming, this has not been easy.

Now the nests are virtually all in the village itself, where the mature trees can be found in long-established gardens. A few nests remain in the vicarage garden, part of a conservation area. Even they are not safe because the church, in a remarkable display of public materialism and lack of vision, applied to build in the vicarage garden. Fortunately the application was turned down, but on another occasion the rooks may not be so lucky.

Several more nests can be seen in the garden of the old squire's house, now converted into an office block, and a few more are in the garden of a nearby farm. In our brook meadows, in old willows, we have a mini-rookery of four or five nests, but that is about it – which means that the rook population is probably at its lowest ever.

In a neighbouring village the birds are so desperate for housing space that a new rookery with three nests has started in a recently planted wood, in which the young trees are only about 20 feet high.

The decline of the rook is not simply a local phenomenon; it has happened over much of Britain during the last forty years. In 1947 it was estimated that there were 1,413,000 nests in Britain. By 1980 the figure had fallen to just over 850,000 (there have been no new figures since). In eastern Scotland numbers continued to be high with rooks almost reaching plague proportions. Indeed the largest rookery in Britain is to be found at Hatton Castle, Aberdeenshire, with nearly 7,000 nests.

Rooks have done well in Scotland for years and as long ago as 1424, James I of Scotland introduced an Act to exterminate the rook. Fortunately he failed. But in East Anglia things are different. If numbers continue to fall there, a case could even be made for the regional protection of the rook, in a few years' time.

The decline of the rook is disappointing for other reasons too. Until recently rooks were part of country tradition. A rhyme used to be recited in the spring: 'Four seeds you have to sow, one for the rook and one for the crow, one to die and one to grow.' Rook pie was also eaten, a dish that was said to be tasty and a way of preventing hair from turning grey.

In addition, rooks were important in weather forecasting. When rooks fly from their nests and fly straight, umbrellas can be left at home; but if they twist and turn on leaving their nests, rough weather is approaching. If they are late leaving their nests and then stay close to the village, it will rain.

Oh, I forgot, for those who cannot identify the rook from a crow, the solution is simple: if you see a single rook, it's a crow, if you see three crows – they are rooks.

15

Diversification

Time passes too quickly. I actually like winter, but already we are contemplating opening the farm up again to visitors for the summer season. It is our way of trying to find additional money as farm incomes continue to fall. We had hoped to spend the winter tidying up and organizing a display of bygones in the old granary, but there remains much to do before opening day on Easter Monday.

I still have bad dreams about the very first day we opened to the public. The whole village was invited, to make it something of a community occasion. About sixty people were enjoying themselves, sitting in the sun and drinking tea, when a rat suddenly trotted coolly out of the barn and made for the nearest group of visitors.

Now what do you do when a rat tries to introduce itself to your friends, causing children to scatter hysterically? It is hardly a good advertisement for future business. There was no farm dog in sight; my brother had disappeared into a pigsty and so there was only one thing to do; taking great care not to spill my tea, I jumped on it (please, no letters from the European Rat Protection League).

But what do you do then, when you are standing on a rat, surrounded by tea-drinking villagers? My nephew stealthily fetched a bucket and then, with a deft back-heel from me, removed the offending rodent. Maradona would have been proud.

More drama followed soon afterwards. For the first time in my life I was tossed. What made it particularly embarrassing was that I was not tossed by Zebbedee, our friendly Murray-Grey bull, but by a cow. A hornless cow had just calved and I was simply carrying out a casual inspection of the new arrival to determine its sex. All of a sudden I found myself flying though the air. As soon as I managed to scramble to my feet she charged again. Fortunately I was able to beat a hasty retreat. She bruised my ribs, but no other damage was done.

It made me reflect on my lucky escape. Thirty five years ago my father was tossed and gored by a bull with horns. He was only saved by old Jim, a First World War veteran, who drove the animal off with a pitch-fork. It put Father in bed for several days and he has had intermittent back trouble ever since. So perhaps with visitors coming to the farm we should forget 'Beware of the Bull', as Zebbedee is so good natured. Instead we ought to display 'Beware of the Cow' – the trouble is, all the cows look the same at a distance, good or bad.

The final problem linked to the opening of the farm concerned Cedric, our magnificent Leghorn cockerel. He was the spitting

image, or, more accurately, the crowing image, of the cockerel which used to introduce the Pathe News at the cinema. One evening he vanished. We searched high and low and put his disappearance down to a hungry fox. Anger at the loss alternated with sadness, until the following day when my father went to collect the eggs from the deep-litter shed and Cedric miraculously reappeared, looking tired but splendid. The bird had apparently set his heart on 300 captive layers, in preference to his legitimate couple of free-range cohorts. The over-romantic cockerel must have sneaked into the shed when my father had collected the eggs the day before – by the time he re-emerged, he was too tired to crow.

If Cedric's health is suspect, so is mine, for a totally different reason. The day after the opening of the farm I went to meet friends at my local pub for dinner – dinner for me is still at midday. Outside the front door was a notice saying: 'Sorry, no bar meals served on Mondays.' So I shrugged my shoulders and went home hungry. It was Tuesday.

16

A Sign of Spring

Spring has definitely arrived. I announce this not because the daffodils are out or the swallows are on their way, but because Badger has paid us a fleeting visit. 'Badger' Walker, from Derbyshire, always says, 'I'll see you in the spring' – so if he has been to see us it must be spring.

The reason for Badger's visit is not simply social as he has a most unusual sideline for a computer engineer – he is one of the best hedge-layers in Britain. He wins prizes; he works with unending energy and he never stops talking – about badgers, birds, country artists, country writers and country poets – he's read them all, he's seen them all and, if they are still alive, he knows them.

His nickname comes from the fact that he loves badgers. He watches badgers, he searches for badgers and perhaps in an earlier life he was a badger. He is never happier than when rootling about at the bottom of a hedge, although when he visits our spreadeagled hedges things are a bit different: 'When I come here I don't lay hedges – you expect me to lay trees.'

But although Badger's arrival is the first sign of spring, nobody told the weather forecasters. The north wind howled across the nearby prairie, bringing with it Arctic temperatures. This gave us a problem: the only way to stay out of the wind was to stand behind the hedge that we were going to cut down and 'lay'.

Perhaps the wind would die down. While we waited, we went to look for frogs. We successfully reintroduced the frogs seven or eight years ago, and there they were in the farm's largest pond – our second sign of spring – 150 frogs enjoying a mass orgy. It is our best year for spawn since the 60s. Sadly annual yields of frog spawn receive no EC subsidies. There is little incentive for farmers in the general countryside to look after their frogs or hedges and in modern agro-speak they are both signs of 'inefficient farming'.

Badger was impressed with the frogs, so we retreated behind the hedge again to discuss their reintroduction and to warm up. It is an odd life being a frog; to spend the whole winter in mud at the bottom of a pond, then to wake up and breed – or, if you are out of luck, wake up and get eaten by a heron.

A car stopped and a tanned gentleman got out. It was Tony Fitzjohn, who for eighteen years worked with George Adamson in Kenya. He has reintroduced lions and leopards to the wild, so we immediately returned to our wild, reintroduced frogs.

Fitzjohn did not seem too impressed. He is currently rehabilitating the 1,000 square mile Mkomaze National Reserve in Tanzania and has cleared hundreds of miles of bush roads. He needs a light aircraft to fly over his rolling acres to check his lions, elephants and zebras; it took us two minutes to walk round the pond to check the frogs. By the time we were back in the hedge it was still too cold to work, so we headed for the pub.

Strangely, although Fitzjohn is doing urgent work in Africa, the frontline for conservation is here in the West. Mkomaze still has a virtually intact eco-system, with a great variety of wildlife. In Cambridgeshire we are down to protecting our last few frogs from 'efficiency' and development. As Fitzjohn retreated to nearby Cambridge University to discuss the reintroduction of wild dogs to Tanzania, and black rhino breeding enclosures, we returned to the shelter of the hedge.

I shouldn't have mentioned the long-eared owls. Badger wanted to see them, so again we had to leave the hedge and walk half a mile in the bitter wind. We saw two of the owls and I collected a handful of pellets from beneath their usual perch. It looked as if they had been eating little but voles – how cruel – I suggested to Badger that we should report them to Kevin McNamara or the RSPCA. Badger disagreed and suggested trying to get a million pound grant from the International Fund for Animal Welfare to induce the bloodthirsty owls to eat profiteroles.

It began to sleet, so we sat in the car. Then amazingly the sun came out and with it came Badger's collection of axes, slashers, billhooks and a chainsaw. A car stopped – a passer-by wanted to watch. 'If you are hedge-laying,' said the passer-by, 'you shouldn't be using a chainsaw.' Why do people not involved in an activity always know best?

Badger persevered. He cut, trimmed, levered, pushed, pulled, bent, grunted, sweated, swore and used his beautiful holly mallet. In the two-and-a-half hours up to dusk Badger laid twenty yards of large hawthorn hedge. In so doing he had created his own countryside picture, a mixture of traditional craft and living art – not just a hedge but a thing of beauty.

It had been a good day. We had not laid much hedge, but we had lived life at the pace it should be lived.

17

Another Sign of Spring

In the last chapter I mentioned two sure signs of spring: the frogs mating and Badger arriving on the farm with his chainsaw. Now the third sign has arrived: me sitting, grumbling in the living room with both legs straight out in front of me. Yes, I've been skiing again. Last year it was one knee; this year I have really excelled myself and managed to damage both. The wipe-out occurred within 65 minutes of my arriving on the piste. I didn't even make the first ski lesson. So much for *kamikaze* skiing straight off the plane. For some time I have had doubts about the ethics of skiing – the ski runs and the tourist tinsel surrounding them do much damage to a very fragile environment. Now the Swiss Alps have struck back.

It was a totally humiliating experience watching a pensioner ski off to get help, leaving me lying helpless in the snow after doing an involutary somersault at high speed. Soon afterwards he arrived back bringing good news – the rescuer was on his way. Then the bad news came – the rescuer was a Swiss-German who could speak no English. He waved and smiled from the ski-lift; I waved and smiled back. On arrival he pointed at my knees and laughed. Then he did a most extraordinary thing; he put me on a stretcher and trussed me up like a joint of meat, I could not move a muscle. Then I achieved a life-time's ambition, and went down a red-run – head first.

At the bottom of the red-run the Swiss-German stopped; the stretcher with me on it kept going, crashing into his skis and damaging my shoulder. For this service he charged me 100 francs, before putting me on a train in a special section designed for bodies. The body of a German woman was already there. She could speak English and so I had to remember the two golden rules for talking to Germans; don't mention the war and choose something safe to talk about, such as the weather. I don't know what came over me, suddenly I said: 'It's been nice weather since the war hasn't it?' She groaned. Being trussed up on the floor of the train, all we could see were the tops of the mountains. 'Doesn't Switzerland look pretty from here?' I commented. She agreed.

Before they would carry me off the train, at a little town down the valley, they made me pay another 100 francs. I was then manhandled, still on the stretcher, into a Land Rover, with the back down for my feet. A length of elastic was then tied across the back to prevent me sliding out. As the vehicle lurched forwards, the stretcher, with me in it, slid backwards, until the elastic, taking my full weight, suddenly shot me forwards like an arrow from a bow, banging my head on the metal partition behind the driver. Now I had damaged knees, an aching shoulder and a dented head – for this last the driver demanded yet another 100 francs.

After I had paid up, the driver of the Land Rover handed me over to a doctor, a beautiful woman with a name that sounded like Binliner. How can you take anybody seriously with a name like Binliner? Her first words shocked me: 'Take your trousers off' she demanded. Her second words were even worse: 'Take your long-johns off.' For the next quarter of an hour she entertained herself by inducing agony and strapping up my knees. For this little service she did not charge 100 francs, but one hundred pounds. She was the most expensive Binliner in Europe. At least the whole performance made me realize the value of the NHS.

Damaging both knees actually makes it impossible to limp; instead I have developed a hobble. Fortunately I can still drive, so I am making regular tours of the farm in my Daihatsu Fourtrak. It is farming without getting my hands and feet dirty – pausing only to wind the window down to tell my brother to work harder. I am quite enjoying this. I now know what it is like to be an agricultural adviser; you have all the enjoyment of farming with none of the discomfort, fatigue or responsibility.

My Fourtrak worries me. I bought it on the recommendation of a rather large farmer friend. It seemed to me that if a vehicle could carry that amount of weight on the front seat and a sheep trailer at the back, it must be a good buy. Previously I had driven a Toyota Tercel, a splendid little vehicle with an excellent flick-on four-wheel drive, but unfortunately it was not really strong enough to pull a load of sheep. So the Daihatsu seemed to be exactly what I wanted. However, it has one major drawback; everytime I start the engine in the morning, it throws out clouds of evil-smelling white smoke. It went back to the garage for checking. The only visible effect was that the clouds of smoke became even bigger. I have now renamed it the 'Daihatsu Smog'.

It is a constant embarrassment to me; I preach conservation and then gas my neighbours. When the wind is from the east, one neighbour's house disappears completely. When there is no wind, I disappear completely, inhaling great lungfuls of foul fumes. If it goes on much longer, it could become a major threat to my long-term survival on the planet.

To give my lungs and legs a rest I went to a local pub the other evening with friends – it was strictly for medical rehabilitation of course. No sooner were we seated comfortably, than a geriatric jazz band started up, many decibels above an acceptable level. Once the ears had adjusted, however, Amadeus Boldwicket's Red Hot Peppers were really very good.

I looked again. I was amazed to see that the roly-poly lead singer and trumpet player was actually performing while smoking a cigar – in a cigar holder. I blinked and looked yet again. It was no ordinary trumpet player, it was that prolific country writer, shooter, teacher and raconteur, John Humphreys, looking in desperate need of an oxygen mask and a pair of herringbone corsets. Every time he hit a high note, he looked down his trumpet and went cross-eyed – I hope he does better when he looks down the barrels of his twelve bore. Despite this the music was excellent.

If John had been born with a silver spoon in his mouth, he would have been a farmer. If he had been born with a muck shovel in his mouth, he would have been a peasant like me. He had neither, and so he became a teacher. He is a good teacher, but the hours of teaching have also allowed him to follow his other interests – country interests – traditions, folklore, shooting, conservation and the Fens.

A few years ago, instead of buying a new car, he bought seven acres of fen, on which he did a most unusual thing for Fenland; he planted trees, osiers and Norfolk reed. Now that seven acres boasts a mixture of country pleasures: skating in winter, birdwatching, fishing, shooting and, on hot summer afternoons, snoozing. Each shooting season the little wilderness gives a hundred pheasants and a hundred ducks, while each bird-breeding season it has families of waterfowl, warblers and assorted songbirds. John Humphreys' love for the Fens shows itself in two beautifully written books – *Poachers' Tales* and *Days and Nights on Hunter's Fen*. So how does this countryman get the time to carry on all his pursuits and interests? The answer surely comes from one of his favourite Fenland quotes: 'No point in getting old unless you grow crafty.'

18

Lambing and Eric

I suppose it is a sign of the times that lambing on the farm is no longer dictated by the traditional market. Getting the lambs into the butchers' shops to coincide with new potatoes and mint sauce is a thing of the past. We now plan lambing to coincide with Easter, when members of the public and schools begin to visit – it is part of our new diversification harvest. Then, all the visitors can stand by the sheep pen sighing, 'Ohhhhhhhh arrrn't they sweet?'

Even after that our lambs are not whisked off to join the red currant jelly in the autumn, as soon as the school visiting season stops, for we also use them as conservation tools. They are our mobile lawnmowers for autumn grazing on our seven acres of hay meadow experiment. They have to graze the meadow, low and hard, to encourage maximum germination of assorted grasses and wildflowers the following spring. By the time the large lambs are ready to go, I am actually quite sorry to see them disappear into the sunset. Because of this I am frequently told that I should pull myself together; there is apparently no room in farming for sentiment. I disagree; sentiment ensures that livestock are treated with respect; it helps to preserve landscapes and it conserves wildlife as a matter of course. That is why our farm is attractive and some other farms that lack sentiment have been turned into prairies.

Lambing has meant that over the past three weeks, while most of the population have been curled up around their hot water bottles counting sheep as they nod off, I have been getting up at all hours of the night to check real sheep in the maternity ward. It has been a successful lambing, averaging just over two live lambs per ewe.

We only have a few sheep – ten ewes. But as sheep are labour intensive, a few demand just as much attention as many. They still have to be dipped and shorn, and during lambing some quite literally have to have a helping hand.

Most of the praise for good lambing goes back to last autumn and Rambo, the borrowed ram. He did his job so well and enthusiastically that three ewes gave birth on the same day. The record woolly Romeo however, was Eric, a neighbour's Suffolk ram, whose reputation travelled far and wide. During the summer he would sulk during his enforced celibacy and any unprepared visitors to his farm were likely to get chased, butted, or worse. But once autumn came he was happy and his exploits became legendary. On one occasion, three years ago, I took our ewes down to him, with my father. Amazingly Eric managed to introduce himself rather eagerly and intimately to four young ladies before we had got the back of the sheep-trailer up again. For once my father was almost lost for words, finally claiming that somebody must have been giving Eric 'Sanatogen' instead of a mineral lick.

All the exploits of Eric and the banter which helped to spread them would not have mattered, apart from one thing. The postman was, and still is, also called Eric. This led to a great deal of confusion and alarm in some quarters. As they heard the postman's footsteps approaching down the garden path, old ladies would hide under the breakfast table, while some young ladies would fling the front door open and greet Eric with a smile. I would like to take this opportunity to say quite openly that Eric the postman is a man of the highest integrity and principle, and as far as I am aware he has nothing in common with Eric the ram; furthermore, he delivers my letters punctually at ten to seven every morning. Eric the ram has now gone into involuntary retirement at the local Wood Green Animal Shelter. That was a wise move, for after Eric's long and vigorous life, if ever he had appeared in a butcher's shop it would definitely have been a case of mutton done up as lamb.

The first night of my sheep watch was exciting. As I walked into the farmyard at about 2.30 a.m., my little lurcher, Bramble, suddenly growled and then took off at top speed. There was a crash and a bang, and a Kevin (a fox) swerved right, then left out of the farmyard and left again into the farmhouse garden. Bramble followed at speed; he lurched right and then he tore straight ahead, at full throttle, across the road and halfway across a field before he realised that he was only chasing dewdrops and had been completely outwitted.

The high speed body-swerve of Kevin had been most impressive. It reminded me of a haddock weaving in and out of the seaweed as the trawlermen – the haddock hounds – approach. I often wonder what

Kevin McNamara MP, the patron saint of foxes, thinks about those of his Hull constituents who chase fish all over the North Sea with their boats and nets. And then what does he think about over-fishing in the North Sea? Of course there is one big difference between fox hunters and fishermen – the haddock hounds use radar, to make sure that few of their victims get away.

19

Rats

I hate rats. I suppose I shouldn't, but I do – even more than magpies.
In fact, the only two creatures in God's creation that I really loathe
are rats and snakes. Snakes I will tolerate, as there are so few of
them, but at the moment we are being overwhelmed by a great
plague of rats, which, if they continue to multiply, will demand a
modern-day Pied Piper.

It is the worst invasion for years and it seems that everything
around the farm that can be burrowed into, or hidden under, has
become home for a rat, or a family of rats. I suppose it is several mild
winters and hot summers that have caused the population explosion,
which has led in turn to stealing food, fouling corn bins, destroying
bale stacks and ruining the deep-litter shed. As a result they must
go. But how do we get rid of them in an acceptable way?

Old Charlie, who once worked on the farm, had a hatred for rats
that now makes mine seem very mild. He considered the gin trap
to be too good for them. Instead he would mix broken glass with
cement and pour the mixture down the holes.

I don't think we will become that extreme, but we must find
a method of efficient rat eradication. It is strange to note that
whatever barbaric method is used against rats, nobody seems to
complain. Normally cruelty to animals activates the 'cuddly bunny
syndrome'. Cruelty to rats arouses nothing.

Surprisingly, the brown rat is not a native of Britain. It originated in Asia and arrived here only in the eighteenth century.
Consequently, one of its common names is 'the Hanoverian rat'
and George II was one of the first people to appoint a rat-catcher.
The main reason why rats have to be caught is that they breed so
quickly. Indeed the sex life of the rabbit is almost leisurely and
puritanical by comparison.

The famous nineteenth-century naturalist J. G. Millais wrote:

'If we take it for granted that a rat has a litter eight times a year; that she gives birth to her first litter on Jan 1st; that each litter is composed of seven males and six females; that each female born within the year has a litter when she is three months old and subsequently a litter at the end of every six weeks; by the end of December one rat will have been responsible for the birth of the enormous total of 35,004 rats.'

Although Millais's final figures and the survival rate are inflated, his calculations show the problem with startling clarity.

So what do we do? We don't like using poison, because of the tawny owls, and we will certainly not do what a friend in a nearby village did recently. She dislikes killing, so she cage-trapped her rats and released them on the other side of the village. I'm sure the rats were highly delighted; I'm not quite so sure about the people who lived there.

An old rat-catcher I know has suggested that we should turn the unpleasant task of rat-catching into an enjoyable sport. He says: 'I have no respect for the pests. I did most of my rat-catching in the Second World War for the War Agricultural Committee. Most of the corn was still stacked at that time, after being cut by binders, and as many as 50 or 60 stacks would stand in the yard of the larger farms and they would get infested with rats. Our only poison then was arsenic and we daren't put it in stacks before they were threshed, so we had to use ferrets.

'We put wire round the stacks and put 20 ferrets in at a time – very hungry doe ferrets – and we used to stand around with sticks and dogs and guns and kill the rats as they bolted. We'd usually get about 100 rats a day. A friend of mine once killed 966 in five days from stacks of barley.

'Another way was to catch a live rat and cover it with tar before releasing it back into the stack – within a few days all the other rats would have left. Boards covered with bird lime were good too. Those rats that became stuck would squeal and fight among themselves before the dogs killed them.'

Ground glass, arsenic, bird lime and tar all sound a bit gruesome to me and ferrets might prefer the hens to the rats. Instead, I wonder if there are any relatives of the Pied Piper still living in Germany – he could lure them away to a place where they could do no damage, such as the Houses of Parliament. Then newspapers could hit the jackpot – they could run a 'Spot the Rat Competition'.

20

Hedgerow Hide-and-Seek

Ever since the first days when men kept cattle and grew corn, farming has been changing. Some of the changes were based on 'progress' – real advances in stocking, cropping and husbandry. But some changes resulted only because of farming fashion.

This summer an unacceptable fashion of modern farming will again be clear for all to see: the flail mowing of hedges right through the summer. In the days of mixed farming when cows and corn went in rotation, hedges had a purpose; they kept in grazing animals and when the plough helped turn grass into grain, the hedges made good windbreaks. Recent studies have revealed that hedges also helped cereal growing in another way, for they provide excellent areas in which hibernating ground beetles and ladybirds, the enemies of aphids, can survive winter. We still have hedges around our small Cambridgeshire farm and we never have to spray for aphids. During the recent hot summers many prairie farmers had terrible aphid infestations in their crops and had to spray. In our fields ladybirds kept us aphid free. One summer day in 1989, when neighbours were busy spraying, we quite literally had a ladybird on every ear of wheat – it was astonishing.

In the old days hedges had a use and were cut by hand – they were laid. Hedge-laying was craft, a skill passed on from one generation to the next, and it took place in the winter, when the land work was done or the soil was too wet to allow work in the fields to continue. Now, on many stockless farms, particularly in areas such as East Anglia and East Yorkshire, hedges are simply a nuisance; unwanted bygones that serve no purpose and are just kept 'tidy'.

Of course, those hedges that still exist are often the mere battered and bent remnants of all those hedges planted at the time of the Enclosures, and they remained in place until the Second World

War. Since then however, thousands of miles of hedgerow have been removed. The great removal took place allegedly to allow farming to become more efficient – so that large machines could work large fields, the argument being that modern machinery could not work at their best in small fields.

A modern-day 'tidy' hedge makes a sorry spectacle. Each year it is flail mowed until it becomes a battered apology for a hedge with a short back and sides. It becomes thin, low and full of gaps. To make matters worse hedges are often cut in full summer and I have seen them cut in May, June, July and August. The fashion has grown from the fact that there are now gaps in the farming year, particularly between spraying, spreading and drilling (sowing) times, and so the farmer is often desperate to give his men something to do. Consequently the order is given: 'Get the hedger out and go and do the hedges.'

The flail mower is put on the tractor and the hedgerow massacre begins. It really is a massacre, for not only do the hedges get battered, but birds' nests get broken, fledglings are mangled, hedgerow saplings are snapped and the numerous food plants of insects, bugs and beetles are destroyed. This is interesting, for if a group of teenage hooligans were to go along a hedgerow smashing birds' eggs and breaking young trees, they would be labelled 'vandals' and punished in a court of law; yet some farmers are just as irresponsible and they break no laws at all.

Directly after harvest is another fashionable time to get the hedger out. This causes less instant death and destruction; instead it strips the hedges of all the wild berries and fruit, thus denying many of our birds food to get them through the winter. This harvest hedging is not malicious – it just shows that many farmers these days simply do not think. They are responding to fashion, or taking the easy option, instead of doing what is right, or what is best for the countryside and the other creatures that depend on it.

The sad thing is that hedges left, or managed sympathetically, can be a great asset to any farm. They look attractive; they are good for game (pheasants, partridges and hares) and they make excellent wildlife corridors for all kinds of fauna and flora. In addition, in a normal year they should not, and need not, be cut until February. This year, those of our hedges that needed cutting were cut mechanically in February, when no harm could be done to wildlife, and of course we also laid a length of hedge by hand with Badger. Most of our hedges however, were left uncut – some did not require cutting and others we have 'let go' and we enjoy them being large and unkempt. In the spring and early summer they are a mass of 'may' and blossom – hawthorn, elder and crab apple;

63

summer sees birds nesting and many butterflies; autumn provides a spectacular wild harvest of hips, haws, hops, blackberries, sloes and crab apples, and winter sees flocks of feeding fieldfares and redwings.

We do not have a monopoly of love for hedgerows of course, as there are many caring farmers whose efforts seem overshadowed by the prairie hooligans. John Wilson of Suffolk, a winner of the Laurent-Perrier Wild Game Conservation Award has magnificent hedges and does not cut them until after Christmas. Last summer I visited another large and attractive farm, in Shropshire, run by Richard Mayall, his wife Anne and daughter Ginny. Richard Mayall is a pioneer of organic farming and runs a highly mechanized 770 acre farm, using large, modern equipment. Yet the farm is attractive with small fields, high hedges and plenty of woodland. His husbandry completely destroys the argument that modern day farming cannot operate commercially using small fields. Richard Mayall's largest field is 35 acres and his average field size is just 18 acres. Recently he has been letting his hedges grow taller; there are hedgerow trees and cutting does not start until January to allow the birds to eat the berries. He is philosophical about the whole issue: 'Small fields are worth the price. You have to ask "Can you afford to live in the environment you want?" Up to now we have, and I hope and pray we will always be able to live in it. There is no doubt that your acre costs of doing everything come down if you are working on a prairie – to me the price is too high and I'm sure the price for posterity is too high.'

At the moment the government is talking about saving hedgerows by placing two or three hedgerows per parish under 'Hedgerow Management Orders'. This would be to protect important hedgerows and pay the landowner £3.00 per metre (what's a metre? It should be either so many awful Ecu per awful metre, or so many wonderful pounds per wonderful foot or yard) for properly laid hedges. This means that he would be paid every time he laid it – about once every 20 years.

Unfortunately, as usual, this plan seems to be too little too late, and seems to have come from an urban mind. To save the last of Britain's old hedges and to help landscape and wildlife, cutting should be banned from May until August. All hedgerow removal should be subject to planning controls and those farmers who have cared for their hedgerows should be paid, not one-off payments, but annual payments, both for management and as a reward. Perhaps then, fine hedgerows will become fashionable again – a fashion to be welcomed.

21

Still More Rats

Those people who have kindly sympathized with the state of my knees now have another condition on which to pour their concern: my back has gone. If this carries on, I could have nothing left in working order by next Christmas.

The back, like the knees, went in a most embarrassing way. A visitor approached with the news that there was a dead rat on display in the goose shed. What an unfortunate beast to have surfaced there, with the geese present. Four manic hissing ganders, one manic hissing goose and four hysterical goslings had met a very stupid rat. Soon it was a very dead rat.

Once the geese had been released, the problem was to remove the rat without any bank holiday visitors noticing. As soon as the family were ogling the ducklings, I ducked low into the goose shed, stretched out with a spade to retrieve the offending corpse . . . and then it happened. I could not move.

I had the rat, but I was bent double, locked like an old man of 90. I shuffled out. The family were no longer ogling the ducklings, but were staring in amazement at me. Predictably, the smallest boy asked at the top of his voice, 'Mummy, what's the funny farmer doing walking like that?'

The mother looked as manic as the geese. 'Oh, he's got a rat,' she screamed. Twenty pairs of eyes turned and focused on the rat; my attempt at surreptitious body-snatching had become a public spectacle. Strange to say, we failed to sell many cups of tea that afternoon.

The following day we chose an alternative to arsenic and ferrets, we decided to hold a meet of the Bird's Farm rat hounds in the deep litter shed. I supervised; my niece Lena blocked the escape holes and started digging (the sort of sexual equality we like in the country), and the three dogs, Husky, Rinty and Bramble, dug, dived and darted in canine bliss.

Husky is the most skilled ratter, a cruncher, which is easy for a hyper-active collie-alsatian cross. Bramble, the lurcher, is a shaker, which is fine until he loses his grip in mid-shake and a live rat goes flying through the air at head height. Rinty, the labrador, is a diver – he dives paws first, before deciding whether or not to bite. So the rats usually bite him first and the other two dogs have to pile in to save him from humiliation. In less than an hour the dogs caught 25 rats – they thought Christmas had come early. There is no surer way to win the loyalty and friendship of a dog than to take it ratting. For weeks afterwards obedience is assured by simply saying 'Rats'.

I suppose some people will consider rat-hunting to be cruel. Those who are offended are welcome to come and live-trap my rats. Then they can take them to start a rat refuge, or send a crateful to the RSPCA or the League Against Cruel Sports, with my compliments.

Because of our current infestation we have reluctantly decided to poison. We just hope that we can get to the bodies before the cat, the owls and, of course, the visitors.

22

Foxes Yet Again

What is happening to me? First it was my knees, then it was my back and now it appears to be my brain. I hope this tome doesn't become a succession of medical reports, but the other breakfast-time I received such a surprise that I almost fainted headfirst into my bowl of porridge.

This shock to my system occurred when I opened my post – not a bill, but the latest edition of the RSPB's journal *Birds*. There, in black and white, was the admission that capercaillie numbers on the Society's spectacular Abernethy estate in Scotland have plummeted because of fox and crow predation.

On neighbouring estates, where keepers are active, the capercaillie is holding its own; as a result the RSPB is to 'experiment' for three years with a policy of controlling foxes and crows. On this occasion there was no press release, or interview on the Nine O'Clock News to accompany the revelation, but at least it is a step in the right direction. I suppose the RSPB's reluctance to publicize the problem caused by predators stems from its large urban membership.

How do you persuade people who have never seen a fox at work, or a crow raiding a nest, that these attractive creatures can cause problems when their numbers become too high, particularly when a variety of pressure groups and misguided individuals seem to suggest that predators no longer predate?

Let's hope that the RSPB's new realism spreads to the crows, magpies and foxes of the Ouse Washes and the Somerset Levels, and also to the peregrine falcons of Anglesey. They are currently driving the beautiful roseate tern away from Britain – an example of one protected species preying on another that is not only protected, but also endangered and in steep decline.

*   *   *

It may be easy, telling the RSPB how to solve its problems, but here at Bird's Farm we also have a problem – foxes. We have so many that if the population keeps rising we will have to change our name to Fox Farm. Virtually every day foxes visit us, and since Christmas we have lost more than 30 laying hens, 8 ducks, 6 silkies and 5 guinea fowl – a subsidy to the local foxes worth more than a hundred pounds.

Last week I even had to move into the farmhouse as a fox guard. My father, at the age of 77, must be getting workshy, for he suddenly decided to take my mother on holiday for a week, leaving me in charge of the poultry. At 5 a.m. on the first day, bedlam broke out; geese were cackling, hens were squawking and the dogs were barking. Quite unconcerned, Kevin (the fox) strolled up to the deep-litter shed and had a look through the window. Then he casually walked over to a pen containing a goose and gander until the hissing gander made him retreat. Kevin appeared to be checking every single henhouse and shed on the off-chance of a meal. But by the time I had crept out with the dogs, the fox had vanished; Rinty and Bramble did not even get its scent.

The next morning at the same time, Kevin was trying to dig into the Cochins' run (the Cochin is a rather large and attractive breed of hen). This time the dogs did pick up the scent and ran around frantically in ever decreasing circles, but again the fox had disappeared into thin air. That afternoon I made for the usually occupied fox earth and managed to catch five cubs unawares, playing in the corn. As I stood by the hole, they simply looked puzzled and calmly trotted underground within a foot of me. The next day my brother did even better, he actually picked one up. But outside the earth were the remains of pigeons, hares and a pheasant – no farmyard ducks or guinea fowl in sight.

The following day, at the other end of the farm, I found guinea-fowl feathers and another earth, under an oak tree, with five more cubs. As I left the vixen was watching me, her head fringed by the wildflowers of our experimental hay meadow. So we have at least two families of cubs on just 113 acres. The crunch is that there are too many, but I find them so attractive that I cannot persuade myself to remove either earth. I'm glad the RSPB is now made of sterner stuff; it is a case of don't do as I do, do as I tell you to do.

Just as I was having tea yesterday there was a knock on the door. It was a didecoy selling 'organic manure guv – only three quid a bag'. 'No thanks,' I replied, 'we've got a machine on the farm that makes it.'

He looked puzzled. 'How does it work?'

'We put grass and hay in one end and organic manure comes out of the other.'

He obviously did not believe me. 'What's it called? he asked.

The answer was simple. 'A cow', I replied.

He looked totally bemused. My father might have been on holiday but I could actually hear him giving the same answer – funny thing, genes.

23

Bloated

In summer my thoughts inevitably turn to food. I love salads; I can never get enough of them and, ignoring the lashings of salad cream that I invariably add, they are not only delicious, but very healthy too. Strawberries are another favourite: to celebrate my first plate of them each year, I add evaporated milk and condensed milk to the usual sugar and cream. If any reader doubts the merits of such a sickly sounding cocktail, they should try it.

The dish also creates an excellent excuse for further indulgence: an open tin of condensed milk cannot be left unused indefinitely, which means that this particular combination has to be eaten again and again until the tin is emptied. Life can be so hard.

Asparagus is my vegetable love of early summer. I have a prolific asparagus bed but, sadly, an assortment of thistles, groundsel, buttercups and bindweed also find the spot attractive. I have treated them with salt, soot and weedkiller, but still the weeds seem to thrive. If anybody can tell me a simple way of keeping an asparagus bed clean, without much bending, I would be most grateful.

My mind was on food the other day when I was telling friends how lucky they were to live near a traditional village baker. Visions of warm, crusty, freshly baked wholemeal loaves floated before me. 'Oh, we don't eat brown bread', they replied simultaneously, 'the husk retains all the harmful chemicals. What little bread we eat is white, the only healthy type there is.' They had read an article which claimed that bran, oatmeal and brown bread, all of which I had believed to be healthy, are in fact bad for you.

There are many other examples of the prevalent food nonsense. One is soya milk. This poor substitute for real cow's milk is now said to contain aluminium. What are all those health-conscious vegans going to do? A local in the village pub had the answer. 'I'm buying soya milk', he told us. We were all baffled until he explained: 'I thought it would be a cheap way of getting a new frame for my greenhouse.'

A few days later came another bombshell – beer causes cancer, as do low cholesterol diets. Up to that point I had been trying to follow a low cholesterol diet, but that day I set about restoring the balance with a fried breakfast and a chocolate eclair – not at the same time of course.

As a result of all this foolishness about what we should eat, my extremely late new year's resolution is to ignore all food scares. I am going to eat what I like, when I like; at least that way I will live and die happy.

I do not usually make new year resolutions at all, but last year I decided to get up every morning at seven. This year I decided that such a regime was damaging my health and so I resolved that from the first of January I would not rise until 8 a.m. With amazing self-discipline I have managed this, although I do wish Eric the postman would try the same thing.

I also endeavour to have a snooze after dinner, for at least half an hour – the midday meal being dinner for me, as it is the largest meal of the day. Researchers have claimed that an after-dinner nap prolongs life and increases contentment. I am very content and am a year older than I was last year at this time – it works.

The other day I met a reader of my column in the *Daily Telegraph* who was very encouraging. He informed me that as soon as the

paper appears in the letter box, he and his wife almost fight for it. The winner then rushes to the loo to read my words of wisdom in comfort; apparently my Farmer's Diary causes much merriment and sympathetic agreement.

My feelings of intense self-satisfaction were very short-lived however. A letter dropped into my letter box, in which another reader informed me that I was the only blot on an otherwise excellent publication. I am apparently, one of those 'pygmies of the media' and my main crime is to engage in the 'character assassination' of leading politicians and 'prominent personages' who, the writer of the letter believes, are overflowing with integrity, intelligence and public service.

I was aggrieved for two reasons: first, a few years ago I visited the rain forests of Zaire where I saw members of the pygmy race. Unfortunately these little people were all about the same height as me. Consequently not only am I a media pygmy, but in certain lights I could also be mistaken for a real pygmy. Friends have tried to lift my spirits by saying that 'small is beautiful' and pointing out that many of the greatest men in history have been 5 ft 5 ins, such as Nelson and Maradona. But it is no good, I have convinced myself that I am indeed a pygmy, though I wonder what real pygmies might think about this.

The second reason for my concern is that the only people I usually criticize are politicians. I have met a lot of impressive, talented people in my time, but few of them have been politicians, many of whom are arrogant, self-opinionated and not very well informed. Now if an arrogant, self-opinionated, not very well informed person chooses to go into public life, why should he or she not be criticized?

W. B. Yeats had the right idea. He wrote: 'Politics, for a vision-seeking man, can be but half an achievement, a choice of an almost easy kind of skill instead of that kind which is the most difficult.' And: 'I find the infinite triviality of politics more trying than ever. We tear each other's character to pieces for things that don't matter to anybody.'

For years I corresponded with an old man who lived on the edge of Exmoor. He was a wit, a cynic and a good friend. He should have been a professional writer but, for lack of other opportunities, he sold biscuits. He summed up the relationship between politicians and ordinary pygmies perfectly: 'The journalists refer to us, the lowly ones, by the synonym 'grass roots'. Well, Robin, you are a farmer's son and I am a farmer's cousin and we know what happens to grass. The beasts walk all over it and, with their omnivorous jaws, they keep it short. Once they have exposed the roots the beasts continue to walk over them and, to use a long word, fertilize them; they walk right and they walk left but to the grass roots it is all the same, they are fertilized on.' I agree totally with the wise words of my now departed old friend.

In some respects the present Tory government has been a good one. It has accepted challenges and faced up to responsibilities that other governments would have ignored in order to curry favour with a fickle electorate. However, its record on agriculture, conservation and the environment can be summed up in one word – pathetic. Sorry, two words – absolutely pathetic.

So I have just made another even more belated new year's resolution; if criticizing our awful MPs for their quite disgraceful environmental record makes me a pygmy, then a pygmy I shall happily remain.

24

Snowdrop

The summer has turned into a very sad one; Snowdrop has had her litter of ten little piglets, but the stress and the heat nearly killed her. Two little females have gone to a Rare Breed centre and two we are keeping ourselves – Snowdrop II and Crocus. We respect our animals and treat them with kindness, but we also have to try to make the farm pay and so Snowdrop has had to go. She was loaded on to the cattle truck and sent to market, leaving me feeling completely guilty.

I feel just as bad when we send cattle to market. Despite thousands of years of domestication, the cow is still a herd animal, yet cattle are rounded up, separated from the herd and sent to market and then bundled off to the slaughter house.

This process is experienced, too, by sheep, pigs and horses and they all feel stress; scientific studies carried out in both Britain and Australia confirm this. The stress is obvious: indeed, I am always disgusted whenever I see a lorry crammed with sheep hurtling along a motorway, as I am when I see lorries packed with crates stuffed full of hens.

So why all the ritual and unfounded fuss about the cruelty of 'blood sports' when the transportation of live animals in bad conditions takes place so openly? Britain's double standards baffle me. I believe that all animals and birds should be slaughtered on the farms where they have been reared, either in mobile slaughterhouses, or in permanent structures on the larger farms. The dealers and butchers would then bid for meat, not live animals. It really is time that the carting of live animals for slaughter is stopped. Yet sadly with the EC now in full swing standards and care will sink even lower, with British animals being transported to all parts of Europe in even greater numbers – including horses. The thought of

British horses suffering the indignities and cruelties of Spanish and Italian markets is appalling, though why should people get excited about horses and not cattle, sheep and hens as well?

All this confirms my view that there are numerous urban animal-illiterates working in the Ministry of Agriculture and Conservative Central Office who are simply not aware of the consequences of their own actions and policies. Colonel George Stephen, the chief executive of the International League for the Protection of Horses is not amused: 'They have no standards – they have regulations but they are rarely enforced.'

This was confirmed for me the other day by my brother. We in Britain fall over backwards to carry out all EC regulations, but in some other parts of the EC the rules are ignored with gay abandon. In Greece he saw lambs with their feet tied together, having their throats cut at the side of the road. Are the Greeks bound by the same EC legislation for hygiene and humanity as we are, or are they not?

This reminds me of a simple explanation of how the EC works:

The Germans make the rules.
The British keep the rules.
The French bend the rules.
The Italians ignore the rules.
The Greeks and Portuguese don't know that any rules exist at all.

There are also rules for a perfect and an imperfect Europe. In a perfect Europe:

The British are the police.
The French are the cooks.
The Germans are the mechanics.
The Italians are the lovers.
And the whole thing is organized by the Swiss.

In a nightmare Europe:

The Germans are the police.
The British are the cooks.
The French are the mechanics.
The Swiss are the lovers.
And the whole thing is organized by the Italians.

We had a bird scare on the farm the other day, which we did not solve the Greek way. When anybody tells me of a young bird out of its nest, my advice is always to leave it – the mother knows where it is, and if it gets taken by a fox, well that is nature. So, when I found a small bird of prey beneath an old magpie's nest, after a high wind, did I leave it alone? No, I took it home as it looked so vulnerable – rather like a predatory snowball. It was a young kestrel.

I phoned the fire brigade, the tender duly arrived and the four helpful and enthusiastic firemen put their ladder to the top of the field maple tree and the nest. We then noticed three other chicks out of the nest, one almost fully-feathered, and one half down and half feathers. My fluffy friend had obviously tried to join his brothers and sisters out of the nest too early. Two were returned to the nest, where an even fluffier one was still in residence.

The return was a complete success, and up to a week later the three chicks, now well feathered, could be seen on the edge of the old magpie's nest. So the incident had a happy ending. It had a happy ending for the firemen as well – by going to the aid of the kestrels they managed to miss an inspection. So both they and the young birds were lucky.

25

Countryside Rape

Cambridgeshire must be the rape centre of the world. There have been vast flowering tracts of the stuff during the past month. Within a ten mile radius of the farm it seems almost as if a third of the land has turned a dazzling yellow.

I always know when rape is on flower. (In my part of Cambridgeshire things are 'on' flower, not 'in' flower. I wish the rest of the country would talk properly.) My chest tightens, I feel lethargic and I get headaches. My father managed to farm for fifty years without any chest problems – now he gets hay fever as soon as the rape is flowering. My brother is the same and a neighbouring farmer usually gets so bad that he has to spend a week in bed.

Of course assorted NFU spokesmen and some sections of the farming press claim that rape causes no problems and they accuse critics of 'farmer bashing'. In that case then, many wheezing farmers are bashing other farmers, with plenty of justification. If there are individuals who really believe that rape is harmless they are very welcome to come and stay in my house next rape season.

It is not just humans that are affected. My vet has had several cases of horses with respiratory problems caused, he believes, by rape. Another vet, at Huntingdon, a town surrounded by a sea of yellow, is convinced that rape affects not only the lungs, but the whole metabolism of horses – my subjective view related to humans, is his objective view related to horses.

It is hardly surprising that rape can have this effect on people and animals. It is well known that the plant contains several toxins and some strains of rape have been known to poison deer and hares. Many farmers growing rape also use large quantities of chemicals as the crop is very susceptible to disease and insect attack. In addition, they spray heavily to clear the land of cereal weeds, because the sprays do not affect the rape; consequently rape is used to 'clean' the ground for next year's cereal crop. This is obviously not selective spraying; it is lazy, tin-can, spray everything farming, regardless of need. In view of all this there is one extremely interesting question that has yet to be answered; is the irritation and lethargy caused by rape due to the pollen, or harmful chemical residues on the pollen? Nobody seems to know the answer and, what is even more alarming, nobody seems to want to know.

The reason so much rape has been grown is simple. It has attracted large subsidies from the European Community; judging by the vision and planning normally associated with Europe, there will presumably soon be a rape mountain.

For the sake of the local inhabitants, both man and beast, no more than 10 per cent of a farmer's land should be put down to rape and no block should be larger than 25 acres. This would allow better dispersal of the pollen and the various nasties that may accompany it.

Recently I went to Worcestershire to talk to a group of farmers and landowners. It was probably a painful experience for them; for me it was a revelation. For some reason I had previously missed Worcestershire in my travels. It is a most attractive county; it still has trees, hedges and grass meadows – in welcome contrast to the prairies of East Anglia. What was even better was the scarcity of rape. Within 24 hours my breathing was back to normal and my lethargy had vanished. It was short-lived of course; on returning to Rape Country all my symptoms returned and I again became a wheezing, slumbering wreck. I even fell asleep during a One Day Cricket Test on television – unheard of and unforgivable.

In normal circumstances I take drugs every day to control my asthma. What puzzles me about medical conditions is the fact that societies are often formed to enable sufferers to join together to discuss their ailments. Inevitably there is an Asthma Society – I am not a member. I can think of nothing worse than sitting in a room with assorted other asthmatics, coughing and spluttering and discussing the condition of our wheezes.

Disease must be a national fascination. While driving to a machinery sale the other day some unfortunate soul on the radio was explaining why she was forming a society for people who pass more wind than usual – or to put it more bluntly, for people who fart a lot. She wanted to get together with other sufferers to talk about their mutual problem – can you imagine it? It sounded like a lot of hot air to me. I wonder if donkeys can join? If so I will give our donkey membership for Christmas; she qualifies easily.

26

Fair Play

Life continues to be very odd. Just when I had got the cricket bat out of the wardrobe, ready for my first game of the season, I twisted my right knee again – getting out of bed. I suppose there is only one answer to that, but a whole summer spent in bed, watching the Test matches on television, does seem rather a waste. So I got out the strapping again, which enabled me to use my right leg sufficiently well to reverse my Daihatsu Smog into the gatepost. My ego was shattered; I had thought only women drove like that.

To be fair my Daihatsu Smog no longer deserves its name. After writing about its evil emissions a nice man from Daihatsu phoned and the problem was solved almost immediately with the fitting of an 'anti-smoke plate'. Quite why the garage that sold me the machine could not have done that in the first place remains a mystery.

Sad to say, no sooner had my Daihatsu Smog lost its smoke, than it became a Daihatsu Aquarium – I left the window open during a thunder storm. However, it did prove conclusively that Daihatsu floors are quite water-tight. Finally it became a Daihatsu Doorless, as I reversed out of my drive to check the sheep with my door open. Unfortunately large gateposts and driver's doors do not get on awfully well, so I found yet another function for baler twine.

The disaster happened shortly before I was due to go to Appleby Horse Fair. Now, I am sure that most gypsies, didecoys, scrap dealers and tarmac specialists, are very honest, but I didn't really fancy attending the largest gypsy gathering in Britain with my car door held on with baler-twine. Consequently, the local Daihatsu dealers were contacted again. They were most relaxed about the problem – forget the Horse Fair – forget towing the sheep for shearing – they might be able to get a door within three weeks or three months. They seemed so laid back they could have been almost horizontal.

However, the nice man at Daihatsu headquarters had the answer again – within two hours he had found a door. The baler twine came off and a new door went on; what a very, very nice man. I must just remember to shut the door before driving off in future.

I always enjoy Appleby Horse Fair, when I manage to get there on the right day. The actual fair day is the second Wednesday in June, but the assorted gypsies and travellers arrive seven days before, for a whole week of horse-trading and celebration. Last year I managed to arrive on the Thursday after, just in time to see a stream of caravans leaving. This year I arrived on time, on the Tuesday, in blazing sunshine, although having come without earrings, tattoos or a beer belly hanging over my belt, I did feel a little underdressed.

The appeal of the fair lies in its traditions, its vitality, and in the way it cocks a snook at modern, sanitized, homogenized, urban Britain. Where else does the internal combustion engine take second place to the horse, or the poacher unashamedly skin rabbits on the roadside? It is not a gathering where they take much notice of EC regulations, or even the Highway Code.

Horses were being washed in the River Eden, in the town centre, before being trotted back up to Fair Hill, where buying and selling and just watching were in full swing. There were horses of all shapes and sizes, for trotting, riding and cart-pulling – black, brown and piebald.

One old fell farmer goes every year. 'It's a good day out and I sometimes buy a horse or pony for riding round my sheep, or hiring out to holidaymakers', he told me. 'Judging by the wads of fifty pound notes changing hands, the recession hasn't hit these people.'

I asked one knowing old boy how on earth some of them made so much money. 'They'll sell anything,' he replied, 'anything that's not screwed down.' From the amount of second hand tack and farm tools for sale, he was probably right.

Fortune-tellers are always well represented. I wondered about seeing one of the assorted Gypsy Rose Lees to ask them about the likely effects of the recent CAP agreement on the small farmer. In one caravan I noticed that there was already a pale, well-dressed gentleman gazing into a crystal ball, as a wizened old woman revealed its secrets. From the back he looked just like John Gummer.

When one extra fat shirtless gentleman walked past the caravan

of Romany Star, she was most helpful: 'I'll tell you your fortune for nothing, mate. You'll have twins.' Yes give me Appleby Horse Fair rather than the Royal Show every time.

In the evening there was harness racing. I have never understood the interest of the gypsies and fell farmers in trotting horses; I like to see a horse gallop. Harness racing seems unnatural and the horses race with their ears flat and pointing backwards, as if they dislike it too. In fact I would much rather see pig racing. Perhaps I should get Snowdrop II and Crocus into training.

27

Sing a Song of Summer

Although the summer has many weeks to run, it is already one that I will remember for a long time. My garden pond is full of froglets; the swallows are nesting in the barn; cuckoos have been calling as if demented; I have been tossed – by a cow – for the first time, and, most important of all, a pair of song thrushes have successfully reared their young in my garden.

Young song thrushes may not cause much excitement to many people, but over recent years it has seemed to me that thrush numbers, both mistle and song thrushes, have plummeted – yet another traditional part of the countryside slowly fading away.

It is not only the song thrush itself that I have missed, but also, as its name suggests, its song; for the song of the 'throstle' has been part of the backcloth of an English summer since before the poetry of Chaucer. Through the ages poets have praised its melodic, twice sung song. Tennyson wrote:

> Summer is coming, summer is coming.
> I know it, I know it, I know it.
> Light again, leaf again, life again, love again,
> Yes, my wild little poet.

In a moment of mellowness even Thomas Hardy praised the song of the thrush:

> At once a voice arose among
> The bleak twigs overhead
> In a full-hearted evensong
> Of joy illimited . . .

The song of the mistle thrush, on the other hand, is not to be welcomed. When it sings from the top of a tall tree it is said to be singing 'More wet – more wet'. Hence its name of 'Storm Cock' for calling up the rain.

But what has caused the decline of the thrush? In my garden the answer is simple. Over the last few summers magpies have systematically hunted my hedges and wilderness for nests and fledglings. This year has been different, every time a magpie has perched at the bottom of my garden it has been met by a hail of hot lead. I have missed each time, but now the black and white marauders give my garden a wide berth, and the thrushes' successful nest was hidden in the ivy where the 'pies' once perched.

Before anybody complains of my cruelty, I should point out that my gun terrifies me every time I fire it, almost as much as it does the magpies. The barrels are pitted and it only has one hammer. On one occasion I asked a well known gunmaker what I should do with it. His answer was simple: 'Hang it on the wall and use it as an ornament.'

My view that magpies are partly responsible for the decline of the song thrush was confirmed to me while on a recent visit to the Isles of Scilly. I did not see one magpie and as a result the islands appear to be full to overflowing with songbirds, including many almost tame thrushes.

Unfortunately for the thrush, the British Trust for Ornithology confirms that the populations of both song and mistle thrushes have dropped sharply in the last thirty years, in both woodland and farmland: 'Using the figure of hundred for the population in 1962 – the song thrush population on farmland now stands at forty-one and in woodland forty-four. The mistle thrush is doing slightly better, with seventy-nine for farmland and ninety-three for woodland.'

The BTO gives three main reasons for the decline, apart from magpies – cats, slug pellets and cold winters. Suburban cats and pampered cats can be great destroyers, as can the gardener who dowses his garden with weedkiller, insecticide and slug bait. It is ironic; although the farming community receives much abuse for polluting the environment, the average sanitized suburban garden is far more polluted than farmland, with assorted chemical sprays and additives. Yet birds in the garden need insects, creeping things and sliding slugs and snails. If their food source disappears – so do the songbirds that feed on them.

Hard winters are the other great thrush killers. The severe cold of 1962–3 probably reduced the thrush populations by as much as a half. Similarly the winter of 1981–2 killed off large numbers. So, the secret of keeping thrushes in the garden is simple; clods of dirt should be thrown at the neighbour's cat whenever possible; the birds must be fed during a cold winter, and gardens should look natural and healthy, not like those from a spray manufacturer's dream. Finally, and most importantly, War – fair or foul – should be declared on the magpie.

28

The Poetry of Progress

God! I will pack, and take a train,
And get me to England once again!
For England's the one land, I know,
Where men with Splendid Hearts may go;
And Cambridgeshire, of all England,
The shire for Men who Understand;
And of that district I prefer
The lovely hamlet Grantchester.

Rupert Brooke wrote these lines in Berlin over eighty years ago. They come from his most famous poem 'The Old Vicarage, Grantchester', where Brooke once lodged for just three years. It is a fine poem – pastoral, lyrical and satirical – and it has ensured that Rupert Brooke will always be identified with Grantchester, the village, its people and its losses caused by war.

The Old Vicarage remains, inhabited by Jeffrey Archer and his family, as does The Orchard, where Brooke first lodged, and his name can still be seen on the war memorial in the churchyard, among a list of more local Cambridgeshire names – Pauley, Plant, Greygoose and Blogg. It has a simple inscription too: 'Men with Splendid Hearts'. His name is on an even longer list of war participants in the Village Hall; few people in the village can now remember the individuals behind the names, or even the war that took so many Cambridgeshire lives.

But would Rupert Brooke really want to be remembered in Grantchester? And would he, or could he 'take a train' today? He would have a problem – the local line disappeared under the axe of Dr Beeching years ago.

Certainly other villagers have no hesitation in thinking that

Brooke would not appreciate the delights of modern-day Grant-chester. One of them, Professor Neville Willmer, Emeritus Professor of Histology in the University of Cambridge has even written a poem, 'The New Heritage Grantchester', a parody based on 'The Old Vicarage'.

> God's? Hell! I will not here remain.
> I'll leave old England once again.
> For England was the land I knew
> Where men with splendid hearts once grew.
> Now, college men show signs of rot,
> Being selfish swats or wrecked with 'pot';
> So Cambridge now and Papworth too
> Have 'labs' for men who hearts renew.
> Away with this! I will bestir
> And quit the modern Grantchester.

At every garden, hedgerow and field the Professor sees some new abomination. Rupert Brooke began his poem quite simply:

> Just now the lilac is in bloom,
> All before my little room;
> And in my flower-beds, I think,
> Smile the carnation and the pink;
> And down the borders, well I know,
> The poppy and the pansy blow.

Things have changed, for Professor Willmer starts his poem less picturesquely:

> Just now the peas are being sprayed,
> To freeze in packs of proper grade;
> And from the little brook, I think,
> There wafts a nauseating stink.
> While in the meadows, you must know,
> No pimpernels nor pansies grow.

The appeal of the seasons has also altered. One of The Old Vicarage's most famous sections reads:

> Unkempt about those hedges blows
> An English unofficial rose;
> And there the unregulated sun
> Slopes down to rest when day is done,
> And wakes a vague unpunctual star,
> A slippered Hesper; and there are
> Meads towards Haslingfield and Coton.
> Where das Betreten's not verboten.

Today's version has a more familiar and unwelcome ring:

> Rarely about our hedges blows
> An English unpolluted rose;
> And when the stubble-smoke-stained sun
> Sinks down to rest when day is done
> It wakes a vague, unpunctual lamp,
> Of yellow sodium; then damp
> Mists shroud the motorway by Coton
> Where das Betreten ist verboten.

Read separately the poems are interesting and amusing, reflecting the times in which they were written. Read together they are frightening, for they bring home the damage that has been inflicted on the countryside since the time of Brooke, as well as the pressures that have been imposed on the rural communities within it.

My own village, where I was born and still live, lies next to Grantchester and so I have seen many of the changes at first hand. In my childhood, just after the Second World War, the world of Rupert Brooke lingered on. In the summer, with other children from the village, I would regularly cycle to Grantchester, over an old bridleway. It ran along a low ridge through fields of hay, oats, wheat and barley, bordered by a profusion of wildflowers – poppies, cornflowers, field scabious, yarrow, and many more. To the north, the outline of Cambridge could be clearly seen – the University Library, Great St Mary's Church (the University church) and of course King's College Chapel. To the south were fields and meadows with high hedges and sentinel hedgerow elms. High up in one of them I found my first kestrels' nest and in a large field, after hay-cart, I discovered the concealed beauty of young skylarks about to fly.

The small fields by Grantchester itself held horses and grazing cows, and moorhens lived by a stagnant pond. Then came the village – a mixture of small cottages from which men went to work on the land, and large houses belonging to retired professional people and college dons, wanting peace and seclusion. The church was large and well kept, with its clock no longer stuck at ten to three, but the chapel was small and poorly attended, with time running out. For smart undergraduates and visitors, cream teas could be taken at the Orchard, among its well pruned fruit trees, while the ordinary village men obtained their entertainment on a small cricket pitch surrounded by clumps of long grass, buttercups and cowpats. The main street meandered like a river, slowing all the traffic, and by one sharp bend stood The Old Vicarage, even then attracting Brooke devotees as well as camera toting tourists.

The river was one of the main attractions. Byron's Pool, cool and still, with the music of water flowing over a weir and the sound of summer in the breeze. Birds sang from the overhanging riverside trees – ash, willow, sycamore and horsechestnut – and dace and roach flashed and darted beneath the surface. It was once a favourite place of both Byron and Brooke, where they swam stark naked.

With more modesty I learnt to swim in the shallows of the Granta where it winds through Grantchester Meadows, and where courting couples strolled, or rolled in the long grass. After days in the harvest field, father too would make the journey, to swim away the dust and sweat of labour. They were good days, and then Brooke's poem needed little amendment.

Today the same summer journey shocks the system. The start of the bridleway is now of tarmac – tidied for suburban minds. It is followed by largely treeless tracts of land where chemical farming rules over uniform plots of high yielding cereals. Then, as the songs of the remaining larks are drowned, a chasm opens up, not of 'green gloom', but of noise, fumes and speed, as a motorway now slices through the parish boundary.

At last, close to the village is a hedgerow, with an oak, an ash and a skeletal elm – all the other elms vanished from the landscape long ago; victims of Dutch Elm Disease and agricultural grants. Then comes the village itself – a terraced house with solar panels, a weedless lawn, a spotless Porsche; the chapel has become an artist's studio and even the village school has been converted into an upmarket house. Then, at the old Rose and Crown, both the sign and the building have been tarted-up – sorry – have a new incarnation. Surprise, surprise, it is now called the Rupert Brooke; but at least he did drink there, so the few remaining villagers from Brooke's era claim. The pub is now popular with a new generation of undergraduates and Brooke's poetry adorns the walls, so that customers can read while eating their quaint old English food ('ratatouille' and 'chilli con carne'). There is another gastronomic delight, a 'Brookeburger' – 'a quarter pound of 100 per cent pure burger in a toasted sesame bun'. It almost goes without saying that there are no chips for sale, only 'French fries'. But who knows, it could help to inspire another literary masterpiece – 'And stands the clock at ten to eight? And is there junk food on my plate?'

The blacksmith closed down years ago, but a garage thrives, doing repair work and selling Hyundai cars. There is a new style, out-of-place telephone kiosk and assorted double-yellow lines and signs – the legalized graffiti of traffic departments with little imagination or aesthetic feeling.

Byron's Pool has also changed. I visited it a fortnight after the start of this year's fishing season. Neither the noble lord nor Rupert Brooke would want to swim there now. The local Environmental Health Officer is quite definite: 'Anybody wanting to swim in the river is mad. It is full of sewage effluent. A few years ago a sample went to be tested – it had so many organisms in it they threw it away, it would have taken too long to analyse.' But even before reaching the water a modern day Byron or Brooke would be in trouble, he would have to tip-toe through the fishing litter, and risk entanglement in discarded nylon line. One piece of debris was most appropriate to the literary associations of the pool – a graphite fishing spool's throw-away cardboard box 'Manufactured in Hong Kong by Shakespeare'.

Fortunately, although the changes are real and often ugly, some aspects of old Grantchester can still be seen and felt. The village remains an interesting mixture of local and newcomer, rich and poor, educated and GCSE failure. There are farmworkers, car salesmen, accountants, college dons, a barrister and Jeffrey Archer and on the whole they all get on. Old style country cottages with daisies in the lawn can be seen over flowering hedges and the old Cambridgeshire accent mingles with those of an elecutionist's dream.

There are a few old-timers too, who still remember Rupert Brooke, or at least stories about him. Eighty-nine year old Gladys Osborne has lived in the village all her life: 'I often remember my father talking about Rupert Brooke,' she says, 'he was a quiet man – he didn't show himself a lot and kept himself to himself – he'd go and have a drink in the Rose and Crown with his friends from Cambridge now and again. The Old Vicarage was neglected then, all overgrown with trees and rambling roses. Now it's all smart and tidy with Jeffrey Archer. It was a dear little village – no one stuck-up or snobbish – everyone knew everyone else. It's still nice to live here, but people aren't so sociable. They only play darts in one of the four pubs now, that shows you how it has changed. There were more sheep in those days and there were meadows full of cowslips and lady's hair – now they've all been ploughed up. I was sad when the school closed down – that should be an important part of every village. The chapel's gone too. It's not so peaceful now either – we can hear the blessed motorway when the wind's from that quarter.'

Another old villager, George Rogers is also eighty-nine and he remembers actually seeing Rupert Brooke: 'I lived next door to the Orchard when he lodged there. I would see him walking down to the Old Vicarage. I remember asking my father why he had long hair – he said it was because he was a poet. It wasn't as long as hair gets today, but longer than the short back and sides we all had then. But the village has changed – for the worse. It's filling with newcomers who don't take any interest in the village. A lot only come because they think Rupert Brooke was born here, but he wasn't, he was only a lodger. It's because outsiders want to live here that the houses cost so much – young village people can't afford to stay here and have to move out. In the old days, because he only stayed here, some people didn't even want his name on the war memorial. They said if all the names of people who had stayed in village were put on, the list would be too long.'

It is surprising how arguments from the First World War still hang on. Another old villager claims that the inclusion of Brooke's name on the memorial was 'political': 'It was only put there to show that officers died in the War as well as the ordinary men of the village – but of course he didn't do any fighting, he just became ill and died.'

In general, the people of Grantchester are proud of their links with Rupert Brooke, but like me they cannot be sure that he would like the the ugly intrusions in and around the modern village, or the way in which the countryside has changed. They are saddened too that his most famous two lines are no longer appropriate:

> And stands the clock at ten to three
> And is there honey still for tea?

How many people have locally produced honey today? I suppose any budding modern-day Rupert Brooke will be racing off down the motorway looking for a Happy Eater.

29

Television Daze

A few weeks ago the wise and understanding Bill Deedes – Lord Deedes – a true countryman, lamented the fact in the *Daily Telegraph* that there was no modern-day A. G. Street fighting the farmer's corner. He is right; but it is not the fault of the farming community. The articulate farmers are there, but the opportunities for them to express themselves in the media are almost non-existent.

When was a farming voice last heard on Radio 4's Any Questions or on Question Time? Occasionally an Old Etonian landowner is wheeled in, but never an authentic A. G. Street type with a rural accent, straw in his hair and mud on his boots. It seems that genuine country people are as rare at the BBC as family planning salesmen at the Vatican.

'What about Countryfile?' I hear you ask. Countryfile seems to me to be a programme which is arranged and presented by urban journalists for an urban audience. There are various minorities with their own programmes, produced and presented by themselves, but country people, and farmers in particular, are not among them.

Of course there is always The Archers, but sadly Ambridge appears to have been taken over by an assortment of sex maniacs, fraudsters and yuppies. The programme does apparently employ an 'agricultural story editor', but what does he do? There is hardly any agriculture included.

It is true that good old Radio 4 still has Farming Today and assorted excellent farming programmes. Unfortunately, they are on so early you have to be an insomniac to hear them. There is a belief that farmers still get up at dawn to milk the cows: most of the farmers I know are still counting sheep, or BMWs in their sleep, long after Farming Today has finished. Why can't it come on at eight o'clock to give us a break from the never ending stream of rehashed, tedious and trivial current affairs?

I do occasionally watch Countryfile, but the omissions and inaccuracies always make me so cross that I vow never to watch it again. The last programme I saw was even stranger than usual. On it, the presenter, an ex-newsreader for children's television, claimed that starlings damaged cereal crops. How extraordinary: we welcome starlings on this farm for the 'leather jackets' they consume in large quantities.

Some of his colleagues are extraordinary too. To me they look and sound more like male models than country reporters. Never mind – we can still turn to the books of A. G. Street, and some of them are just as relevant as they ever were.

I have come to the conclusion that to be a farmer you have to be a masochist. At the moment farming is like banging your head against a brick wall, or in my case a muckheap, as we haven't got many brick walls – and it doesn't even feel good when you leave off.

The public don't understand us; the politicians don't want to understand us; we don't understand the politicians; and as British agriculture gradually slides down the plughole, sucked by EC quotas, restrictions and falling prices, so food imports rise and the profits of the food retailers, particularly of the supermarkets, rocket out of sight. It is a strange, painful world indeed.

'Ah,' you might remind me,' the recent CAP agreement has been worked out and the British farmer has won a good deal, courtesy of the saintly Mr Gummer.'

But is it a good deal? In the past week I have asked a galaxy of 'experts' what the CAP agreement will mean for our farm. None of them can tell me; apparently even the EC officials don't understand what it means. So what hope have I, a simple Cambridgeshire peasant, of grasping it? What do I tell the bank manager next time I see him? And how do I plan for the future? Perhaps I should invite Mr Gummer down for the weekend; he must surely know what he has agreed.

People have been extremely helpful recently and given me an assortment of suggestions for keeping the foxes away from our hens. The most practical is to surround our hen houses with one of the most common liquids known to man. Consequently, just before breakfast, with the larks singing and the cocks crowing, my father creeps furtively towards the henhouses, chamberpot in hand, to do his duty. So far it seems to have worked.

Someone else suggests leaving oxheads out in the fields for the foxes. It might have been a good way in the past; today it would attract Environmental Health Officers even faster than foxes.

30

Dog Days

I feel guilty, for there is one dog who has been almost omitted from this peasant's diary – my brother's dog Husky. He is a good, big, frightening dog, a peasant's dog, with a bark to match his purposeful bound. He only has to run towards any itinerant's van parked outside the farm and the occupants accelerate away at top speed. It is odd how Husky seems to detect an interest that could become light-fingered.

He is an impressive dog. He looks like a cross between a wolf and a husky although his ancestry is more likely to be that of an illicit affair between an alsatian and a border collie. He has a never ending liking for water, and his second favourite pastime is to bite water as it comes out of the hosepipe. His most favourite pastime is to hang on to the bull's tail, where Ben left off. Unfortunately he is so large and his bite so strong that we have to rush to curb his enthusiasm before his jaws clamp shut.

Husky remains responsible for one of the funniest scenes I have ever seen on the farm. The dastardly deed was done during the aftermath of harvest. We were loading straw bales onto a juggernaut for a farmer in the Lake District. The North had experienced a disastrous drought and winter straw for their livestock was like gold-dust, so we shipped our spare straw north. As we had almost finished loading, a sales rep. arrived. He did not walk over the stubble as usual, but drove in his brand new car. He was impeccably dressed with a trilby, sports jacket, moleskin trousers and shiny brown leather shoes – he was straight out of a glossy country-wear catalogue. Brother John stopped to talk, but Husky was not impressed. For me, high up on the lorry, it was painful, as I could see exactly what was going to happen. Husky casually approached the mannequin from behind sniffed the brand new trousers and then, yes, he cocked his leg. This in itself would not have been funny, but Husky did not perform a simple territorial marking, he actually stood, swaying on his three legs, as the entire contents of his bladder gushed out in a never-ending deluge; it was an act of genuine relief. The agricultural male model leapt into the air in astonishment as his leg became sopping wet and warm, then began frantically hopping on the dry leg, as he shook the other, desperately trying to prevent the torrent from draining into his shoe. I laughed until my stomach ached and I nearly fell off the lorry.

Being a big, bad dog Husky is a natural hunter, particularly of small mice. Because of this John had hoped that he would make a good gun-dog to work with Rinty. Out rough-shooting in his first autumn he bounded home as soon as John fired the first shot. It is not much fun being a gun-shy dog and every time he hears a bang, this barking, biting, black monster shakes like a jelly.

Bramble and Rinty remain the real hunters, Rinty with his labrador pedigree and good nose and Bramble with his lack of pedigree and lurcher's speed. They make a good pair, working in tandem – one flushing, and the other chasing – although at times they cannot remember which one should be doing what.

Rabbits continue to be their most common uncaught quarry, but they prefer foxes. The most recent fox hunt started prematurely. An upper-crust lady on The Archers was about to take her dogs for a walk: 'Come on girls – walkies! – walkies!' she said. Although not girls Rinty and Bramble shot up, looking at the radio, puzzled. I had no option but to take them for their Sunday walk early.

Just as I came out of the farmyard I stopped, amazed. For almost directly opposite me a fine fox walked through the hedge. The dogs were amazed too, as was the fox – then, chaos. They began to chase the fox down the middle of the road. The fox quickly skipped back into the hedge, the dogs did the same thing, with one slight difference – instead of following the fox, with noses down, they followed Kevin's (Reynard's) scent in the opposite direction.

Soon the fox was trotting unconcernedly towards the brook, while Bramble was yapping, in full cry, hunting backwards. The dogs arrived at the pile of wood in the old spinney that the fox had recently vacated, just as Kevin disappeared from view in the opposite direction. Why Bramble decided to follow by scent I have no idea; according to books, a lurcher is also a 'gaze hound' – hunting by sight. I think he must be a haze hound – the sight of a fox creates a great mental haze that sends him the wrong way.

Rinty and Bramble's other favourite hunt is in a thick clump of brambles; as they go one side, an attractive black and white rabbit inevitably runs out the other and races for the protection of a pile

of wood. Someone's escaped tame rabbit is living in the wild and making a good job of it. At the end of each unsuccessful hunt Rinty plunges into the brook, Bramble stands and looks thoughtful. I think the black and white rabbit should take extra care.

After every walk Rinty returns soaked to his kennel outside the farmhouse; at the instruction 'Go home Husky', Husky does exactly that, while Bramble returns with me to the cottage. Hot and exhausted he immediately falls asleep on his bean-bag, lying on his back with all four feet in the air.

He is a happy, contented dog and whenever I leave him he greets my return with a flurry of tail, paws and bites. I hope this would meet the approval of W. H. Davies who wrote:

> Still do I claim no man can reach
> His highest soul's perfection,
> Until his life, from day to day,
> Deserves a dog's affection.

One day I arrived home from Norfolk, just after midnight, to find the cottage empty. I ran down to the farmhouse, and there in the living room lay Bramble; he had been knocked over by a car while crossing the main road and looked close to death. His eyes opened but he could not move and his tail did not wag. His head was cut, his legs were grazed and his rump was raw, as if he had been rolled over. I left him to rest, fearing the worst and preparing myself for heartbreak.

Early in the morning I went to him again. I was relieved for he greeted me, stiffly and obviously in great pain, but he was alive and I laid him gently in the car to carry him the hundred yards home. All morning he lay still, until I helped him out for a natural break. Within two minutes he had vanished and an hour later he still had not returned. Had he taken a turn for the worse and crawled away to die?

My search was soon over. There he was; he had already crossed the lethal main road, and with head up was trotting, somewhat stiffly, towards the house where a beautiful young lady spaniel was in season – she was much too good looking to be 'on heat'. Already love had provided Bramble with an instant miracle cure.

31

Wedding Day

Coming home from a North Country wedding the other day I stopped at a motorway service station, for an intake of deep-fried salmonella. While stretching my legs afterwards I noticed copies of a very well-known book for sale, *A Year in Provence* by Peter Mayle, so I bought a copy. It is a volume applauded by many critics; it has become a best-seller and it has been made into a television series; it has won a literary prize and the author has been seen and heard on 'chat shows' galore.

It is a mildly amusing book about a middle-class couple moving to Provence and finding a paradise of eccentric peasants and eating houses. Every activity becomes an adventure; sampling the wine, having the builders in and talking to Didier.

The interesting thing of course is that similar characters and country idiosyncrasies still exist in the British countryside – just – but the many middle-class people who move into our rural villages are so busy commuting to and from nine-to-five jobs, watching Countryfile on television and going to Provence for their annual holidays that they don't notice what is around them.

Within a small radius of my hovel there is Gypsy Jim, whose alcoholic intake is measured by the angle of his cap; the Royal Oak, with exceptional food and a landlady whose bizarre make-up artistry gives her the nickname of 'The Painted Lady' – people travel miles to ogle her, as the till ticks over merrily. Then there is Jack who turns virtually everything into alcohol and Pastor John, a reformed professional gambler who drives himself to tears in the local Baptist pulpit. What Farmer Teddy doesn't know about farming, wheeling and dealing is not worth knowing, and Mick, the local jobbing builder is a master of everything except getting the water out of my bath. Old Bill prefers to live in his garden shed, rather than his house; it is the most luxurious shed in Britain, complete with a chimney and an upstairs. Even my brother John is worth a mention. He has a theory that the farm toolshed should be left in a state of total chaos: 'Then if anybody comes nosing around at night, they won't be able to find anything worth stealing.' The only problem is that when something breaks down, we can't find any tool worth using either, and if anything was stolen it would take us five years to find out.

Because of all this, I think I will give Provence a miss this year – it's more entertaining staying here.

After the potential food poisoning and heart-disease at the service station I tried some strawberries – huge foreign mutations that tasted like their name, straw-berries. Why importers buy such rubbish is beyond me, particularly as the traditional, small British strawberry is such a treat for the tastebuds.

A few villages away an acquaintance has forty acres of his farm down to 'Pick Your Own', including traditional strawberries. He has one major problem however – the strawberries are too good, for as he produces more and charges more, so his takings decrease steadily. Groups of pickers, complete with their own sugar and cream, are eating their way around the field, without apparently regarding their activities as theft. Some even have bottles of water with them to wash the strawberries first. He cannot think how to combat the problem – perhaps he should frisk all customers for sugar and cream before allowing them onto the field, or even weigh everybody, as well as their baskets, before and after.

My trip to the North Country was for the wedding of my niece in the Lancashire village of Crawshawbooth, just up the road from Ramsbottom and down the road from Dunnockshaw. It was much more interesting than a wedding in Provence, being a cross between a modern-day travellers' party and a happy-clappy Christian revivalist meeting. There were leather jackets, pony tails, and it seemed as if somebody had got hold of a job-lot of earrings and nose studs from Rajisthan.

My niece, a vegetarian, married Rick, an artist, who wore leather trousers – the trousers didn't have fly buttons or a zip, but a rather fetching length of green chord. Surprisingly to me, the guest wearing the Animal Liberation Front T-shirt didn't spray the groom with paint – I suppose that treatment is saved up for women wearing fur coats. Music was supplied by a Christian rock group and the bride walked down the aisle to 'Hard Headed Woman', written by Cat Stevens – now known to his friends as Yusef Islam. The bride and groom left the church to a rendering of 'I don't want to go back to Egypt' – explaining, I presume, why they went to Ireland for their honeymoon. The bride gave the traditional speech of thanks and the wedding cake was a chocolate sponge. Fortunately my dear old mother's pacemaker lasted the course, although it did appear to be going backwards at one stage.

If ever I decide to share my house with anybody, apart from my dog, I've already decided on the wedding music – I've always liked 'Nellie the Elephant' and what about 'I've got a lovely bunch of coconuts'?

32

Gentlemen Prefer Hay

I felt quite at home the other day as we had a gathering of Country Gentlemen on the farm, many of whom were in fact women. Members of the Country Gentlemen's Association arrived in large numbers to look at our traditional hay meadow, sponsored by the Association. In addition to indigenous grasses and wildflowers, known to some of our neighbours as 'weeds', they had also come to see Gordon Beningfield and Phil Drabble, who had arrived to take part in a ceremonial scything.

The first problem was to get Gordon Beningfield away from the flowering teasels along the nearby brook. It has been a tremendous summer for butterflies and they appreciate teasels in fields, almost as much as they like buddleias in gardens; all Gordon wanted to do was watch butterflies. He was eventually dragged away, bringing his brand new scythe with him.

The second problem was that the hay meadow should have been cut three weeks earlier; the grasses were dry and sapless, but had been left uncut for the open day. Consequently attempting to scythe the dry stems was like trying to cut rubber with a butter knife.

Phil Drabble had style but claimed that it would have made little difference whether he scythed with the protective sacking on his blade or off. Once he started I could see what he meant. Gordon Beningfield scythed with vigour, rather than style. His greatest achievement was to almost turn Bramble, my long-legged lurcher, into a short-legged dachshund. Fortunately his flashing blade just missed the astonished Bramble.

It was a good afternoon and the experiment to try to re-create a traditional hay meadow is proving to be an interesting one. Sown in the spring of 1990, the wildflowers have done surprisingly well, with vetches, clovers, plantains, ox-eye daisies and yellow rattle all flourishing. A cousin who farms in the Pennines cannot believe what we have done. 'What,' he exclaimed on hearing the news, 'planted yellow rattle! I've spent 20 years trying to get rid of it.'

The meadow grasses have been very disappointing however; sowing in a drought was not exactly helpful. Rye grass, put in as a nurse crop, is flourishing, but Cock's Foot, Timothy, Crested Dog's Tail and Annual Meadow-Grass are all in short supply. If things do not improve we will have to try to plant some more.

Another problem is the invasion of unwelcome wild plants – 'weeds' even to us – around the edge of the field. Hemlock, barren broom and goosegrass are all invading. Consequently we cut the headlands early, hoping to carry off the unwanted plants as hay bales.

In May and early June the field was like a large, flowering garden. Butterflies love it and it has been re-colonized by grasshoppers and hundreds of insects. Already it is showing that, if given the chance, wildlife can quickly restore itself on farmland and the general countryside. The meadow is of farming use too; next year we will cut it for good hay and again this autumn the cattle and sheep will graze it.

The experiment was started as we did not believe that the government's set-aside policies were positive enough. With the help of the CGA we wanted to show that creative set-aside could be of value to both farming and conservation. Tim Allen of the Countryside Commission came to see the experiment early on, and it does appear that some of the features of our scheme have now been included in the Countryside Commission's Stewardship Scheme – so the whole thing has been well worth while.

The mixture of flower and grass seed was obtained from Miriam Rothschild. Now well into her eighties she is still busy trying to get people to encourage dragonflies in their ponds, plant wild pear trees in their woodlands, retain several species of natural roses in their hedgerows, and so on – while still endeavouring to farm for profit at the same time. She is a remarkable woman. It amazes me that assorted political has-beens, as well as some never-has-beens, have been elevated to the House of Lords on the Buggins Turn roundabout, yet Miriam Rothschild who has spent a lifetime doing useful things has not had the recognition she clearly deserves.

The ox-eye daisies have been particularly spectacular this year. On passing Culpeper's shop in Cambridge when all the ox-eye daisies were flowering, my sister saw some even more remarkable flowers for sale – 'Oxide daisies'. It seems that either the daisies, or the shop assistants, had been drinking too many agrochemicals. No doubt Nicholas Culpeper, the long departed herbalist, was not simply turning in his grave, he was spinning out of control.

Something unfortunate has happened in the village. A complete 'listed building' has been stolen. It was not the farmhouse, fortunately, it was the parish pump – officially described as a 'Grade II Listed Building'. No doubt the thief had a ready market for his ill-gotten gain, at a garden-centre or a car boot sale. How incredibly mean and greedy to steal such an interesting historical feature from the village scene. If any reader has bought an old pump recently could they check it? The stolen listed building was a Bamford Universal Pump, made in Uttoxeter, and its number is 7959 Mark 14x. If the small-minded thief is caught, perhaps the judge could introduce him to another listed building in a nearby village – the stocks. I for one would take great delight in throwing rotten eggs and various other farmyard waste materials at him.

33

Gums and Roses

The traditional method of inducing sleep is to lie back and count imaginary sheep. I do things rather differently; the other morning I was sound asleep, when I suddenly awoke counting sheep – not the sheep of my dreams, but real, bleating sheep. My neighbour's garden was a sea of walking, grazing wool – mowing the lawn, browsing the roses and chomping contentedly at the vegetable patch. They were not our small flock, but those of a nearby farmer. He is something of a rare breed, being one who plants trees, retains unsprayed grassland, coppices, hedgerows and keeps sheep. His sheep often seem to get out, but at least they break out on weekdays; our cattle specialize in breaking out on Sundays, particularly when it is raining.

It was the second time in two days that the sheep had dashed a quarter of a mile to squash into my neighbours' garden, evidently considering that flower borders and beds were far better than the grass in their brookside meadow. The farmer was not pleased: 'Tuesday will stop them', he muttered, 'they are going to market.' What a selling point – rose tinted mutton.

I was relieved that they had not jumped over the ditch into my garden, as grazing on my froglet filled lawn they would have ceased to be true herbivores. Fancy that – frog tasting lamb – it would put you off the mint sauce and new potatoes.

So it was up with the sun to persuade the sheep to return to their field. Bramble, like me, was not pleased to be up. 'Scoof' I said, which in normal circumstances has the little lurcher lurching at high speed after rabbits, foxes, cattle and even people. But he was not interested. I have spent years telling him to ignore sheep and he has never chased them. He looked at me as if I had gone mad. Sheep! He would not even look at them, let alone chase them.

'Scoof', I said again, but Bramble apparently saw no sheep, heard no sheep and smelt no sheep. He disturbed a froglet on the lawn and looked blankly into space. 'Thankyou Bramble', I said as I clambered across the stinging nettle filled ditch; it was the first time that I had questioned the wisdom of leaving the ditch wild for the butterflies. Sheep evidently do not enjoy seeing pyjama clad, muttering figures emerging from a ditch, for as soon as they saw me they turned and sprinted back to their meadow like homing-mutton. In a matter of seconds the garden was empty and silence had returned. It was uncanny; had I been dreaming, or even sleep walking? The rose petals and sheep droppings on the lawn confirmed reality.

Normally sheep in the garden would be annoying, not a disaster, but this year it happened the day before the Village Flower Show. Each year my immediate neighbours tend their garden with patience, skill and love. It is weeded, hoed and nurtured; their vegetables grow; their flowers bloom and they invariably win prizes at the Flower Show. I could imagine the 'Arrangement of Three Roses' this year – three browsed briars with wool on the thorns, followed by six half eaten pods of broad beans competing for the vegetable prizes.

It was sad for them, as the Village Flower Show is as important to local gardeners as the Chelsea Flower Show is to professional

growers. Indeed, preparation starts very early in the year when plants are 'brought on' in the greenhouse, to be planted out in the spring. I know, because another neighbour had problems of a different kind: first of all his pansies disappeared; then, as each new herb, vegetable or flower was planted out, it was immediately and gratefully devoured. That neighbour is a large, jolly, rumbustious man, but with each new vanishing pansy he appeared close to tears. Could it be rabbits invading from the fields?

The solution came when I again looked blearily out of my bedroom window early one morning. A half grown brown rabbit was grazing contentedly on my lawn. 'Scoof', I said to Bramble once more, as another rabbit appeared – normally he needs no second invitation to chase rabbits. He looked at me questioningly. 'Scoof', I said again. He seemed to think I had gone mad and ambled after the rabbits with no effort to catch them.

Suddenly the truth struck – they were farm rabbits, belonging to my niece. Normally we have them in a run to activate the cuddly-bunny syndrome in visitors to the farm, but they had escaped and were invading all the neighbouring gardens, including that of the tearful pansy grower, a member of the Horticultural Society Committee. Already it was safe to say he would not win a prize for pansies, three varieties of beans, peas and carrots. To make matters worse Bramble would not chase the offending creatures, as the poor schizophrenic dog had learnt that farm rabbits were different from field rabbits (a lesson the farm cat still refuses to learn).

With the aid of a mink cage-trap and strawberry netting the offending rabbits were eventually recaught. But surely it is time for new classes to be introduced to village flower shows, to compensate the unfortunate gardener, such as: the best naturally pruned gladioli; a dish of rabbit trimmed pansies, and of course a leg of best rose-tinted lamb.

34

Corncrake Odyssey

Today's harvest is a time of dust, noise and frenetic activity. The aim is simple: to get the grain combined as early and as quickly as possible. The change from horse and binder, shock and corn stack,* to combine harvester and bulk grain has been rapid – just one generation. Now the old harvest can only be savoured in a Gordon Beningfield painting, or where a thatcher still cuts wheat with a binder in order to get long straw to enable him to carry on his craft.

Similarly hay time has been transformed. Constable's 'hay wain' has been lost to rural history – overtaken by 'big bales', silage and mowers working as fast as most people can run. As a direct consequence not only have farming practices altered, but so has the wildlife that once shared the land. Just fifty years ago cornfields and hay meadows were in harmony with wildlife – rich reservoirs of wildflowers, butterflies, birds and animals. In my childhood, in the decade after the Second World War the Village Flower Show was held in high summer, that time of pause between hay time and harvest. Then, all those attending the village school would enter the wildflower competition. Armfuls of wildflowers were picked in a never-ending supply of field scabious, knapweed, cornflower, campion, clover, several kinds of poppy, and many more.

Then came spray, power and speed – the fields of hay and wheat were cleaned, cleared and made more productive. The wildflowers and butterflies slowly faded away and the remnants are still disappearing; with them in many areas went the harvest mouse, the grey partridge and the once common brown hare.

But as a boy I was intrigued by an even earlier casualty, one

* 'Stook' and 'rick' in some areas.

which had found even the change from scythe to mowing machine and binder too great – the corncrake. Old men, and even my father, spoke of the corncrake with humour and affection, but it had gone before I could experience the pleasure of following its distinctive, elusive call, hoping for a sighting. How could a bird simply disappear? It is a question now too easily answered, for since 1960 I have witnessed the disappearance of the barn owl, the green woodpecker and the sparrowhawk as breeding birds in my parish.

But for some reason I felt cheated at the loss of the corncrake – I had been denied part of my rural heritage. I still feel the loss, for the corncrake's disappearance symbolizes the pace of change and lack of concern that is still transforming and destroying the British countryside, I believe beyond recall. So, for years I have been intrigued by this bird that, throughout the country, has found the twentieth century just too much to cope with. Each spring I have hoped to hear one call, as it passed through on migration and in countless conversations in many parts of Britain I have been fascinated to note how, like the secretive bird itself, the corncrake has crept in.

My father moved into our small Cambridgeshire farm in 1926 and shortly afterwards he heard his one and only corncrake: 'It was in Tinker's field – men were cutting corn when someone shouted "there's a corncrake in here" – it flew out like a moorhen.' Jim and Charlie, two old farmworkers, have also sadly disappeared, but they too remembered: 'It was a secretive little bird – cunning – you hardly ever saw it – just heard it – they would nest in the hay fields.' 'They were named after their call – they would 'crake-crake' all night long – it would drive you barmy.' The call is a distinctive grating noise, very similar to the bird's Latin name *Crex*. Recently I obtained a recording, clearly reproducing the 'crex-crex, crex-crex' and played it to an elderly neighbour – an 82-year old retired gardener. He recognized it instantly: 'Why that's an old corncrake – I haven't heard one of them for years. Cor, there used to be no end of 'em about round Royston Heath when I worked in Hertfordshire.' Royston Heath is now a golf course.

But memories of the corncrake go back much further, to the time when it was known as the landrail. John Clare (1793–1864), the very much underrated 'peasant poet' from Northamptonshire, knew the bird well:

Were is the school boy that has not heard that mysterious noise
which comes with the spring in the grass and green corn I have

followed it for hours and all to no purpose it seemd like a sprit that mockd my folly in running after it the noise it makes is a low craking very much like that of a Drake from whence I suppose it got the name of Landrake I never started it up when a boy but I have often seen it flye since about two years ago while I was walking in a neighbours homstead we heard one of these landrails in his wheat we hunted down the land and accidentily as it were we started it up it seemd to flye very awkward and its long legs hung down as if they were broken it was just at dewfall in the evening it flew towards the street instead of the field and popt into a chamber window that happened to be open when a cat seizd and killd it it was something like the quail but smaller and very slender with no tail scarcly and rather long legs it was of brown color they lay like the quail and partridge upon the ground in the corn and grass they make no nest but scrat a hole in the ground and lay a great number of eggs My mother found a landrails nest once while weeding wheat with seventeen eggs and they were not sat on they were short eggs made in the form of the partridges not much unlike the color of the plovers the year before last when I was helping to carry yaumd beans [beans gathered into sheaves] which are shorn with a hook instead of being mown with a scythe and stoukd in shoves [sheaves] like wheat as I was throing one of these shoves upon the wagon somthing ran from under it very quick and squatted about the land I mistook it at first for a rat as it hastend bye me and struck at it with my fork but on percieving my mistake I stoopd down to catch it it awkardly took wing and settld in a border of bush I found it was a landrail by its legs dangling down as it flew.

It was also familiar to Thomas Bewick (1753–1828), that excellent wood engraver and countryman from the north-east:

Its well-known cry is first heard as soon as the grass becomes long enough to shelter it, and continues till the grass is cut; but the bird is seldom seen, for it constantly skulks among the thickest part of the herbage, and runs so nimbly through it, winding and doubling in every direction, that it is difficult to come near it; when hard pushed by the dog, it sometimes stops short and squats down, by which means its too eager persuer overshoots the spot, and looses scent ... The female lays ten or twelve eggs, on a nest made of a little moss or dry grass loosely put together; they are pale ash-colour, marked with rust-coloured spots. The young Crakes are covered with a black down; they soon find the use of their legs, for they follow the mother immediately after they have burst the shell.

The corncrake was so well known and widespread that it was mentioned too by Robert Burns, Richard Jefferies, Gilbert White and many more. In the 1880s it was so common that it was still heard on Streatham Common in London.

However, in 1895 those pioneers of bird photography, the Kearton brothers gave a warning of what was to come. In their book *British Birds' Nests*, they suggested that corncrakes were still common, nesting 'on the ground amongst mowing grass, clover, willow beds and standing corn all over the United Kingdom', but added 'the bird sits close, and as a consequence, individuals sometimes get their heads cut off by the mower's scythe or machine.'

By the mid-fifties my small *Observer's Book of British Birds* still gave no hint of the corncrake's demise, although it could no longer be seen or heard in Cambridgeshire; however a far older book in the bookcase of the farmhouse gave a clue. In *Birds of our Country and of the Dominions, Colonies and Dependencies* I read: 'The corncrake is one of the few birds we have which are chiefly known by their note: most of us well know the harsh nasal "arrp arrp", which is, or used to be, so familiar a summer sound almost everywhere; it has been heard even in the remote island of Iona . . . It should not, however, be treated as game, partly because it is a useful destroyer of insects and other vermin, on which it chiefly feeds, and partly because it is not at all common nowadays, so many of its nests being destroyed by the mowing machines . . . The corncrake breeds everywhere with us, even in the Hebrides and Shetlands, while it also breeds throughout Central and Northern Europe, and east to Turkestan, migrating to Africa in winter.'

Over recent years in numerous travels in Britain I seem to have followed the corncrake's disappearance. Farmers and fishermen, crofters and shepherds, from as far apart as Cornwall, the Lake District, Wales, the Cairngorms and the Shetlands have all given me variations of the same theme: 'We used to hear the corncrake – but it's gone. We last heard it five years ago, although one was heard down the valley, so they say, last year.' The corncrake has always been in the next parish, valley or county, or on a neighbouring island, headland or peninsula.

In 1981 I decided that the time for hearing the corncrake as a normal part of an unplanned summer was over. I would have to make a special journey. An old white-haired lady told me how two years before, she had heard corncrakes on the island of Arran and my *Atlas of Breeding Birds in Britain and Ireland* confirmed that they were there. They were not – it was the same familiar story – I had just missed them as their retreat northwards continued, due to the earlier grass cutting for hay and silage and their late nesting. There was one slight flicker of hope, an 'old wifie' who loved 'the wee bird' and who had heard just one, earlier in the year. She spoke with affection for the corncrake, in an accent that almost sang: 'I first went oot in the gloamin, to hear the cuckoo. Instead I heard the corncrake in the brae – it was good of her to let us hear her call.'

At the turn of the century the corncrake population of Britain could have been counted in thousands, by 1978 an RSPB count suggested that it had plummeted to between 700–746 calling birds (males). Ten years later the number had fallen to between 550–600, with virtually all the birds restricted to the Western Isles, with the Uists and Tiree being its last real strongholds. It represented a decline of 15–26 per cent: during the same period the Irish population dropped by an even more alarming 30 per cent.

I never intended last year to be the year of the corncrake, but I decided I had to travel to the Western Isles before the inevitable finally clears the corncrake from Britain. Tiree was the island that beckoned – previously I had seen it as a low, distant shadow from Rhum, but James Cadbury of the RSPB assured me that on Tiree, traditional island life continued – mainly pastoral, with crofting, cattle, ancient hay meadows and corncrakes.

Driving north the reasons for the corncrake's disappearance were clear to see. Fields of grass, shorn by forage harvesters and grazed close by sheep, at a time when the corncrake would once have been nesting. In the fields of standing corn the birds would have received no respite either for the crops were turning, with today's early ripening varieties, and few broods of chicks would now survive the thundering advance of the combine harvester, or the aftermath of fire and smoke.

I made a detour to the village of Helpston the home of John Clare. No corncrake has been seen there for decades. On many of the farms the spray can and flail-mower reign supreme. If John Clare were to return he would no longer write lines of beauty and feeling, his words would be full of bitterness and betrayal.

Further north it was ironical, for there in the northern Pennines I saw traditional hay fields, uncut and full of native grasses and wildflowers. With the help of government grants, farmers have reverted to a limited form of traditional husbandry in a region designated as an Environmentally Sensitive Area. The hay fields so badly needed by the corncrake had returned – but sadly, the corncrake had not.

From Oban, Tiree lies past Mull and beyond Coll, a low-lying island of just 29½ square miles, out in the Atlantic. Its landscape is treeless, looking windswept and wasted; a strange, remote place to be described as a 'stronghold' for the corncrake. The island seemed almost unreal, a mixture of sunlight and sea mist, and around it the ocean appeared to steam.

Tiree is a harmony of moorland, machair and hay meadow, scattered with white painted houses and a sprinkling of traditional thatched Hebridean cottages; sheep graze on the moor; cattle roam over the wildflower carpets of the machair, and the hay meadows guarantee feeding for the livestock in winter.

As I drove along single track roads in bright sunlight all I heard were skylarks singing. Cattle were being driven to new pasture and in a pool of hot sunlight more cows and their calves were walking into the sea to escape from the heat and flies. I stopped and listened – I could hear no corncrakes. An old crofter was taking his sheepdog with him to look at his two small hay meadows, totalling just six acres. He was not encouraging: 'Oh the corncrake; he used to be here in hundreds – everywhere – lovely little birds, but they're getting fewer. I haven't heard one at all this year.'

Another crofter, Hugh MacLean was more promising: 'There were four corncrakes within hearing distance of the farmhouse last week. I've even seen one sitting on the dyke (small 'earthen' wall) crocking away there the other night. It would be sad if we lost them, we are used to the corncrake – we've had more of them this year than we've had for the last four or five years.' His croft covers 26 acres with 50 acres of 'out run' (common land). 'We use the old method of making hay – we use a finger cutter and make haycocks out in the fields – we put tripods beneath them to let the air run through even in bad weather, and then cart them home and make ricks. People go for silage now, that means early cutting, and rye grass – that comes earlier too. In pre-war days we didn't do any harvesting till August and all the fledgling corncrakes were all out and away by then – but now'days the mower cuts right through the nest. Sometimes I've cut the hen off the nest – I didn't know it was there. It makes you feel bad, but what can you do?'

He spoke with a beautiful lilting accent, a mixture of Scots and Irish, about crofting, the island and its wildlife, all of which he loved: 'It would be a sorry summer without the corncrake. People differ in their feelings towards nature. I happen to be one of those who take a close look at nature, but some of the other crofters couldn't care less, they are not interested. But we want the corncrake and everything else we are used to – the phalarope, the godwit – we like to see them.'

I saw my first corncrake on my first evening on the island. The sun was still bright despite mist rolling in from the sea creating strange white arches of dazzling light – like rainbows without colour –

something I had not seen before. A bird flew up from a field of freshly mown hay and passed directly in front of me. It was brown and rufous, with the flight of a moorhen and trailing legs – a corncrake. I was astonished – how could such a bird migrate as far as Cape Province for the winter, only to return all the way back to a Hebridean hay meadow for summer. It dropped down into an uncut field and then I heard it, 'Crex-crex, crex-crex, crex-crex'.

Along the road in more uncut hay there were others. I played a recording of a corncrake calling near one, grasses moved along an erratic course until he appeared, head up and curious. Then he turned away – head down – head up – head down – moving grasses and he was gone.

I heard many others and saw another, calling, surrounded by wildflowers – clover, tufted vetch, ragged robin, spotted orchid, eyebright, buttercup, yellow rattle and daisies. It was how I had always imagined them; a traditional bird in a traditional hay meadow – somehow the two seemed to go together perfectly.

There is no doubt that many islanders are closely attached to their birds. One has a male regularly visit her garden right outside the living room window: 'We love them, unfortunately we called him Maggie, as he walks just like Maggie Thatcher. We saw a hen and chicks one year too – the chicks are very dark, blackish, not like the adult corncrake. We know where they nest – just outside the bottom of the garden – but we don't go near them. There seem to be more this year; they nearly always arrive on my mother's birthday, April 24th, although they were a day late this year.' Outside the garden was more hay together with beds of yellow iris.

But not only did I see corncrakes, hay meadows and traditional farming on Tiree, I also saw ominous signs. Sheep are becoming more numerous and whereas many hay meadows were still uncut in July, some silage had clearly been cut in June. One large field was cut with a drum mower, at more than running speed; any nesting corncrake would not have stood a chance. An islander was worried by the increasing use of silage and its early cutting: 'It has increased enormously in just two years and there is even more this year.' Some crofters without the concern or traditions of Hugh MacLean want to hire, borrow and even buy silage machines in the future. Yet if the island's population of sheep increases and the area of silage expands, then the corncrake is doomed. Not only does it become exposed to hooves and mechanisation, but its chicks and eggs become easy prey to hooded crows and gulls.

Astonishingly, despite the corncrake's precarious position and the government's alleged conversion to 'green awareness', there has not been one nature reserve set aside for the corncrake. What is needed is for the whole of Tiree to be declared an Environmentally Sensitive Area while most of its hay fields can still be preserved with their wildlife – for Tiree's wildlife goes far beyond the corncrake. It would simply mean paying farmers to farm in the traditional way, without suffering financially because of it.

The RSPB could also try to organize a rescue for those nests destroyed each year. Any eggs saved could be put under bantams and the chicks reared in the ESA of the Pennines to try to create a safe haven for corncrakes there.

Not all the corncrake's problems are British. On migration it sometimes falls foul of electric cables; the French still shoot it and some of the habitat in its wintering grounds may be changing. Yet despite this there is little doubt that more could be done in Britain to help the bird survive. It is strange how some campaigns in exotic parts of the world to help the rhino, the elephant and the gorilla, often attract more support and interest than those threatened creatures on our own doorstep.

Last summer gave me great pleasure because of my corncrake odyssey, but it also caused me sadness. On my last evening on Tiree the corncrakes seemed quiet. I heard one; I did not see the bird – there was movement and grasses swayed – what I saw was the shadow of extinction.

35

Snap, Crackle and Pop

These are worrying times – I've started talking to myself. One of the questions I asked myself the other day was 'Does John Gummer read what I write?' I think he must do, for changes that I have been urging over the years are slowly taking place.

It has seemed obvious to me for a long time that if farming, wildlife and landscape are to co-exist in harmony, governments should produce a system of reward for sensible farmers, not through prices and production, which inevitably lead to over-production, but through payments for the way in which farmers farm.

Farmers and landowners should not be paid subsidies, but should be given money for the hedgerows they keep, the trees they have retained, the water meadows left undrained and the field headlands they do not spray. This would encourage over-intensive farmers to follow suit; it would pay the farmer; it would produce smaller amounts of food, improve the landscape and encourage wildlife all at the same time. It would be simple, cheaper than the present EC fiasco and it would keep farmers on the land. The countryside would be alive and well.

I have said all this in various forms for the last ten years, and because of the lack of response I have assumed that my pearls of wisdom fell on deaf ears. Now, however, things are beginning to change. The Government is running a pilot scheme to link wildlife, landscape and less intensive farming. At the moment the Countryside Stewardship Scheme covers just a few areas and a few habitats; what is really wanted is a system of rewards for stewardship and responsible farming to cover the whole country.

Some time ago I wrote about 'experts' who seem to have tunnel vision and little common sense. Now comes a story from

Oxfordshire about a recently graduated zoologist. With various others he was looking over fifty acres of set-aside land. While walking across the field the farmer said: 'All this set-aside is having one good effect, I've just seen my first leveret for several years.' When the farmer was out of earshot the zoologist asked: 'What's a leveret? A type of rat?'

Following my corncrake odyssey I was flooded with letters giving me much fascinating information about corncrakes, plus many memories and sightings. One retired farmer, again from Oxfordshire, remembers corncrakes each summer before the Second World War, and in his wife's old copy of Mrs Beeton's Cookery Book, where there is a recipe for 'roast landrail' (corncrake). The same farmer recently asked a landowner from County Mayo in Ireland if they had corncrakes there: 'Oh yes', came the reply, 'all the usual ones, Kelloggs, Rice Crispies and Roast Toasties.'

I went to tea with a fine old countrywoman the other day, before speaking at the St Neots Local History Society. As she cut the bread a large hole appeared in the slice. 'You know what that means?' I remarked casually, 'there is going to be a death.' At that moment the telephone rang, giving her the news that a friend had just died. It was an extremely eerie feeling.

It must be the season for odd stories. Recently, a friend made a rare visit to Cambridge and overheard two shop assistants talking: 'Where did you go for your holiday?' asked one.
   'Majorca', replied the other.
   'Where's that?'
   'I don't know, I went by plane.'

One of the great pleasures in life is reading stickers, notices and graffiti. Yesterday I saw one which read: 'Wear British Wool – 40 million sheep can't be wrong.' Even better was the notice outside a house announcing 'Guinea-pigs – only £1.20 each'. Underneath, somebody had scrawled: 'Oven Ready – £1.50.'

36

Food for Thought

My catalogue of tribulation continues. After my knees, back and brain, I am now getting fat. The reason is simple: as my knees and back are still rather suspect, I am not burning up the calories that would normally disappear in a summer of work and play. Sadly the brain has not adjusted to the new circumstances and when it identifies food it issues the simple instruction, 'Eat it'.

The problem is magnified by the fact that whenever I visit the farmhouse the appetizing smells of traditional, seasonal, English cooking seem to be permeating the whole house, from the kitchen. Inevitably my mother asks: 'Do you want to try this?', and the brain does the rest. On the last visit it was scones, and as usual she won first prize with them at the Village Flower Show.

It is a year-long calendar of country cooking, from meat pudding in the middle of winter, to raspberries and unpasteurized ice cream now. If I go down to the farmhouse tomorrow I know it will smell of stuffed marrow, or simmering redcurrant jelly. The day after it will be plums, as the Early Rivers come onto the menu. If there is a tastier fruit in the world than a freshly picked English Early River, I have yet to discover it. Of course, on their own Early River plums are not fattening, but in my mother's kitchen they will be eaten as plum treacle, plum crumble, plum pudding (suet pudding with plums inside) and plum pie – with brown sugar, cream and custard as optional extras. The calorie count will escalate and I will have to loosen my belt by another two holes. I am beginning to feel sorry for all those gastronomically underprivileged people who spend their time eating chilli con carne, lasagne and moussaka; they don't know what they are missing. If I had to choose between eating in one of London's top French, Italian or Greek restaurants, or my mother's kitchen, I would choose the tried, tested and enjoyed every time.

* * *

117

It is an incredible plum year this year. All the trees – Rivers, Victorias, Czars and Monarchs – are creaking under their load of fruit, as are the greengages. It is not a question of what we are going to do with it all, it is will the branches crack and break before the fruit is ripe? In our small orchard, as the fruit swells, so the extra weight makes the boughs hang lower, bringing more fruit down to browsing level for the sheep, who have really begun to appreciate the laws of gravity.

With a glut of English plums available it will be interesting to see what happens in the supermarkets. I suspect the shelves will continue to overflow with inferior Euro-plums that look like plastic and taste like sodden polystyrene – it is all beyond my comprehension.

With harvest now upon us and hay bales still to cart we are entering our busiest time of the year. Because of this I will have to do some heavy physical work, regardless of the state of my knees, and so I visited my doctor in the hope of getting some knee braces. He could see my problem and sent me with a note to the Artificial Limb and Surgical Appliance Clinic at Addenbrookes Hospital. It should have been a simple exercise, but wasn't. The clinic claimed that it could not help me without a note from a consultant – waiting list nine months. The fact that harvest cannot wait nine months seemed irrelevant. If you are a bank manager or an accountant, it should be possible to work on with suspect knee ligaments; if you are a working farmer you cannot, without risking further damage. Unfortunately I now have to take that risk – didn't I read somewhere about a 'social charter'? I am already taking that risk at cricket with sensational results – I have been run out twice in three innings.

The other evening I was putting hay bales into heaps, very cautiously, at about half pace, when I became aware of a bird call that I had not heard in the parish since the cold winter of 1963. It was the laughing cry of a green woodpecker up in some old willows by the brook. The disappearance of the once common bird was both sudden and tragic. The cold came and stayed for weeks – kingfishers, kestrels, sparrowhawks, barn owls and green woodpeckers had all disappeared by the time the thaw set in. Sadly too, the woodpecker's disappearance coincided with agricultural change. Trees and hedges were ripped out to make larger arable fields, denying the woodpecker food and nest sites, and fields of permanent pasture went under the plough destroying ant hills by the score, another source of food. Later, Dutch Elm Disease made any recolonization unlikely.

Now, nearly thirty years later, the green woodpecker is back, aided and abetted by tree-planting and, I suspect, set-aside. Hearing the call of the 'rain bird' so close to home gave me much pleasure and, true to tradition, that night it rained. At half speed, it was a good job that I managed to finish heaping those bales.

37

What a Gannet

Thinking of food reminds me of gannets. Although I have been to many of the most famous wildlife reserves in the world and have seen some of the most exotic birds and animals on the planet, I still feel a great sense of excitement and wonder at some of the great wildlife scenes to be experienced in Britain. Among the most spectacular are our great seabird colonies, and the bird that gives me the same thrill today as it did when I first saw it thirty years ago, is the gannet.

The gannet is a magnificent bird. To the untutored eye it is like a cross between a gull and a goose, but it is far larger than a gull, and more graceful than a goose, and it has a large spear-like bill. Apart from the black tips to its wings and its cream coloured head, the bird is pure white – a startling white, the same colour as seaspray on a sunny summer day. The bird's beauty is completed perfectly by its eyes, of a clear light blue. The gannet is roughly the same size as a greylag goose, but more graceful and slender, and when it lifts off to fly its narrow pointed wings give an impressive six foot span. Once in the air it can fly comfortably at 40 mph and in addition it will often glide easily and expertly on the wind, as it lives the life of an ocean wanderer.

I have seen gannets around all parts of Britain from Shetland to the Isles of Scilly, and from the Wash to the Isle of Arran. Each time I see them I feel a sense of excitement and anticipation, hoping to see a dive, as gannets live on a diet of fish which they catch by diving headfirst at speed, like gleaming white harpoons. The dive of a gannet is both spectacular and breathtaking: the bird may be as high as 100 feet, then suddenly it tucks in its wings and falls fast and straight to hit the water in a fountain of spray. On a still day the thud of the impact can be heard several hundred yards away. It has been estimated that when it enters the water it is travelling as fast as 60 mph, the momentum taking it to a depth of 15 feet, and with wings and webbed feet beating underwater depths of 50 feet can be reached in pursuit of fish. If a shoal of mackerel is found, dozens of gannets will dive repeatedly, gorging themselves on the abundant fish – hence the description 'gannet' for a glutton. The dive of a gannet is helped by its weight, as a gannet in good condition can weigh up to 8 lbs; its fat is important to keep out the cold and also as a store of food for hard times.

The British gannet is often called the Atlantic or Northern gannet, to distinguish it from its close relatives the African and the Australasian gannets; another of its relatives is the unfortunately named 'booby'. There are 200,000 pairs of gannets in the North Atlantic, stretching from the eastern seaboard of Canada to north Norway and southwards to Brittany. During the breeding season the birds come ashore, with 80 per cent of the population nesting in the eastern north Atlantic. The largest colony in the world is at St Kilda, with about 60,000 pairs and then comes Grassholm, off the Pembrokeshire coast, with 30,000. In addition there are a number of other famous British colonies, at the Bass Rock in the Firth of Forth; Noss and Hermaness in Shetland; Sule Stack in Orkney and Sula Sgeir in the Outer Hebrides. England has just one colony, at Bempton Cliffs on the Yorkshire coast, just above Bridlington.

At one time gannets also nested on Lundy Island, but ceased to do so around 1909. Traditionally fishermen and islanders around our coast collected gannet eggs and young for food and oil. Salted gannets would help the people of St Kilda get through the winter, they even wore the skin of gannet necks as shoes. But for many years now gannets have been left alone by people, and other predators cause few problems as the birds nest on islands or inaccessible cliffs.

Gannets build their nests on the ground – heaps of seaweed, grasses, flotsam and jetsam, often including pieces of old fishing net. The nests are extremely close together and each female will lay just one egg in April or May. Incubation is most unusual, for the bird actually sits with its webbed feet over the egg; the male and the female both take turns in sitting. The chick hatches after 43–5 days; it is dark, ugly and almost reptilian in appearance. It quickly grows a good coat of dark down and puts on weight rapidly. At this time, not only is the gannet colony a remarkable sight, but also produces a cacophony of cries. The hillside or rocky cliff will be almost white with birds. Some gannets will be displaying, others will be incubating eggs or guarding their young, and all the time the air will be full of gannets, landing, taking off or just gliding in the air currents. Because of their size, when they land there are inevitably collisions, arguments and fights, creating bedlam as birds call, chastise and make contact with their mates. Those people who visit a colony imagining that nature is about harmony and happy families can get quite a shock.

Occasionally a young bird will fall out of a nest and sometimes it seems that the adults do not recognize their fallen chick, struggling to get back; they will attack it or simply ignore it. Sadly, it has to be admitted that although the gannet is a very beautiful bird, it would not win any Mastermind contests. Inded Bryan Nelson, author of the best and most detailed book on the gannet writes 'they are indeed extraordinarily and exasperatingly stupid.'

One day when it is between ten and thirteen weeks old, the gannet chick is simply abandoned by its parents. After ten days of frustration and growing hunger it takes off and flies down to the sea, where it will swim on the surface for two or three weeks, heading south. To start with it is too heavy to take off while swimming and can only fly again after it has lost some of its large store of fat. When it is really hungry it will start fishing instinctively, probably while still on the surface. Soon the young bird will be able to fly and its life of wandering, diving and catching fish will begin. Many first year birds continue moving south until they reach the equator. They return to home waters in their second or third year and start to breed in about their fourth, after some highly ritualized courtship displays.

Several of the gannet colonies in Britain can be seen at close quarters. Probably the most spectacular and the easiest to get to, on a calm day, is Grassholm, nine miles off the coast of Pembrokeshire. Seen from the mainland or from the other Pembrokeshire islands it looks like a distant white dome. But as the boat chugs steadily nearer it becomes clear that the white is a mass of breeding gannets. Originally Grassholm was famous for its puffins, but the shallow soil could not support their burrows and they left. The first small gannet colony started about 1860 and it has increased steadily ever since. By 1964 the number had risen to 15,500 pairs; in 1978 it was 20,000 and now it is over 32,000. This makes it the highest density of breeding seabirds in Britain with over 60,000 adult gannets, as well as a few guillemots, razorbills, gulls, kittiwakes and shags, in just twenty-two acres. The island is looked after by the RSPB and the society's officer for Wales, Roger Lovegrove, is pleased with the increase: 'I expect they will go on increasing until they run out of room. Feeding is not a problem as they range over such a large area. The future for gannets in Wales, and the rest of Britain, looks fine.' On calm days it is possible to get onto the Grassholm, where the gannets, in their thousands, can be seen at very close quarters. It is an unforgettable experience and one of the wildlife wonders of the world.

38

Bramble's Big Day

This time of year is always very busy for Bramble. In the morning, as I write, he sleeps, to get his strength up for the afternoon. In the afternoon he rides on the tractor to the harvest field where, like the good lurcher he is, he chases anything that moves. This afternoon, as the combine harvester devoured the corn he 'coursed' three toads and a frog (they all got away under the straw) though he prefers chasing rabbits and hares. Then in the evening, to recover from his hard afternoon and prepare for the morning, he sleeps again. Quite often in these evening sleeps he chases again, his twitching limbs and muffled barks indicating a much more exciting quarry than frogs and toads, or for that matter, the neighbour's white cat.

Because I am convinced that he is an outstanding dog, fast, graceful, intelligent and beautiful, just like his owner, I recently took him to the Holkham Country Fair. I wanted to enter him for his first lurcher show, in the hope that my modest assessment of him would be shared by others, including the judges.

The Holkham Country Fair is held during the first weekend of September at Holkham Hall in Norfolk, every other year. It is rapidly becoming an important item on the countryman's calendar – not to be missed.

I felt proud walking with my dog among the Range Rovers, green wellies, clapped out Fords and ferrets. Heads turned and people were obviously agreeing with me already that he was an outstanding little dog; certainly their reactions had nothing to do with my scantily clad, nubile cousin Fiona, who was also with me.

At the lurcher ring his rivals were already assembling; long dogs, sleek dogs and mean dogs that would have had the average gypsy reaching for his wad of five pound notes. The lurcher is the traditional poaching dog of the gypsy – a cross between a whippet or a greyhound for speed and a terrier, collie or labrador for intelligence.

Bramble's pedigree, if that is the right word (the Kennel Club considers it to be the wrong word) is a cross between a whippet/lurcher mother, and a Bedlington terrier father, a pedigree Bedlington terrier of Argentinian origin. The result is Bramble, looking like a dishevelled, miniature wolfhound.

A tattooed man with shoulder-length hair seemed to be in charge and soon Bramble's big moment came with the announcement: 'Rough-haired dogs under 23 inches.' Human breeding lines are as complicated as dogs', and as Fiona took Bramble into the ring I remembered that in fact she was not my cousin, technically, but my first cousin once removed – but still, all eyes were definitely on Bramble. The tension mounted, the dogs were walked and trotted and the judge looked them carefully up and down, before feeling their limbs for soundness. Then I heard him say: 'The little dog's got it.' Not only did Bramble get a rosette, but it was red – he had won, my judgement had been confirmed.

The rest seemed to be a mere formality; later, when all the classes had been judged, Bramble would be a certainty for the title of Supreme Champion. Before that moment of glory however, there was more work to be done, with a lurcher demonstration in the main ring, complete with 'simulated coursing'. This was not simply a rag tied to a rope and pulled along in a straight line by a small electric motor, but a lure, pulled through a number of widely spaced rings which made it turn at right angles at high speed.

Bramble had seen nothing like this before and was taken to the start as a 'novice'. The old gamekeeper who had bred him was

doubtful: 'He'll never run you know – it's a waste of time.' The lure was off – Bramble waited – suddenly he twigged what to do and was chasing, beating the other dog easily. The second time he was even better, trouncing a dog twice his size and leaping the fence to greet me, as if to say 'Didn't I do well.' Me, the old gamekeeper and Fiona all puffed out our chests with pride.

Sadly the gap between Bramble's 'First' and the Supreme Championship was a disaster. The judge had changed – what do Welshmen know about lurchers? The Welsh judge failed to give Bramble anything; he was obviously gullible, and it was just because the other dogs were all washed, combed and groomed whereas Bramble had come straight off the tractor. Bramble was not pleased either and as he walked past one stall he cocked his leg over an ornamental tea towel. The rain started falling in buckets, another sign that Bramble had been robbed.

All in all however, it had been an excellent day. Bramble's red rosette now hangs proudly on my study wall – he really is an outstanding dog. Incidentally, I forgot to say that there were just two entries in Bramble's first class, but the other dog was very, very good.

39

Harvest Home

It is always a relief to finish harvest and this year we finished in the nick of time – just before the weather and the combine harvester both broke. Consequently all our grain was sun baked, not needing the drier, and we have plenty of time to repair the combine before next year.

We were lucky, as at one stage it appeared as if an EC conspiracy was afoot to stop us. With just ten acres to go the combine overheated and smouldering dust and chaff actually burnt through the fuel pipe without catching fire. I thought we were very fortunate; my father thought we were very unfortunate. As our New Holland combine is, in reality, an extremely old New Holland combine, he thought that a spectacular fire would have been a good way to get a new one.

No sooner had the fuel pipe been repaired than there was an unscheduled electricity cut, proving yet again my theory that Britain's services are becoming increasingly Third World. All our grain handling, once the combine has been emptied, is powered by electricity and so harvest again came to an abrupt stop.

The next morning an early start was needed to beat the approaching rain and this was made possible by a dewless night. No sooner had I hitched the grain trailer to the tractor than I developed a strange list to starboard. With my medical record over the last few months I thought that some internal ballast tank must have deflated, but a quick glance at my bulging waistline proved otherwise; instead it was a puncture in one of the large rear tyres of the tractor.

We eventually resumed. As the last wheat disappeared into the combine, signifying the end of harvest, a loud clatter of broken metal signified the end of the combine – at least for this year. As the final load was augered into the grain store, the thunder clouds blackened and that night a storm broke, so I was told; I slept like a log content in the knowledge of harvest home.

A good, quick, dry harvest has again left one frustration. As the moisture content of our grain is well below the permitted level, it means that grain dealers buying our corn can safely add water to it, with their sophisticated watering equipment. This will significantly increase the weight of our crops, before they are sold again. In this way the dealers are able to sell tap water at £100 a ton, with our grain. It really is time that premium payments were made to farmers for dry grain. The present system is nothing less than legalised robbery.

The very afternoon that harvest finished, our second brood of swallows left the barn, accompanied by their excited, protective parents. Just one pair returned to the farm this year, from a high of fourteen pairs thirty years ago. Two years ago we were having great problems with our swallows; the hot weather meant high mite numbers in the nests and high temperatures beneath the corrugated iron roof were making the young swallows jump to their deaths. Because of this we wanted to experiment with a new, cooler roof. We approached the RSPB for sponsorship, but they could not afford the £1,400 needed from their £25 million budget. Fortunately Intervet, the veterinary products company, came to our rescue and have shown a real interest in the experiment.

The tin roof was taken off and plastic sheeting (Rockwall sheeting) was put on top of inch thick polystyrene. It has worked; the temperature of the barn has fallen noticeably in hot weather and even on the hottest day of harvest the young swallows suffered no discomfort. In addition, during the winter, we spray the old nests with insecticide (Ectophen soluble) to get rid of over-wintering parasites.

Consequently, to see the second brood leave the nest gave me enormous pleasure – it meant a successful swallow harvest this year too. A summer without swallows is almost unthinkable, yet from the low numbers in the surrounding parishes this year, it seems as if that sorry day may be fast approaching.

All is not quite right with the swallow experiment however – we might have made things too comfortable. As I write, the hen bird is still incubating her third clutch of eggs. I hope she gets the youngsters off safely before the weather really breaks, but it will be touch and go.

Mice also like the new arrangements and are busily chewing up the polystyrene into little balls. In fact they like it so much that they don't come down to be trapped, poisoned or caught by the cat. If only they would chew it up into larger sizes, then we could paint the debris purple and sell it to Tesco's as French and Spanish plums.

I was sorry to hear of the recent death of Gertrude Bugler,* the last living link with Thomas Hardy. Last year in Dorchester I had the privilege of meeting this dignified, elegant, happy farmer's wife whom Thomas Hardy saw as his perfect Tess. Even at the age of ninety-four she had the most striking, beautiful, clear, laughing eyes. It was easy to see how she had captivated Hardy. Her departure is a sad loss for traditional, rural Dorset.

* 6 August, 1992.

40

Harvest and Heaving Braces

Each year we celebrate the end of harvest with the 'horkey', the traditional harvest supper/or, more accurately, 'blow-out'. All those who have helped in any way are invited. This year I have continued a new tradition that I started several years ago – an end-of-harvest breakfast. The day after harvest I stay in bed until half-past eight, before 'trenchering' a massive mound of fatty fried foods. I enjoy it and hope that the annual feast does not lead to an early meeting with the great harvester in the sky. There are eggs, bacon, sausages, potatoes, mushrooms, tomatoes and fried bread, all oozing with fat. This is followed by rounds of toast and marmalade. The calorie count is enormous and my cholesterol level rockets; it would terrify any dietician.

The amazing thing about this breakfast of course, is that although I consider it to be special – a once-a-year treat – during my father's working life he put similar breakfasts away every single day, preceded by a large plate of porridge, milk and golden syrup. Then down would go the bread and marmalade, both home made, which meant that one round was never enough. Now, in his late seventies, father is still active and in good health; it is clear that his lifetime of large breakfasts have done him no harm. Indeed the other day, at seventy-eight, I saw him in the barn, carrying a hundredweight sack of wheat on his back up a ladder, to empty it in the mill. I suppose the reason for his good health is that all during his life, he has burnt off his breakfasts through physical labour. These days he would find the traditional breakfast more difficult to cope with, as much modern farmwork is carried out in the sitting position – behind a desk, on a tractor or driving the combine.

But not only did the farming people of a few years ago have huge breakfasts, they also had 'docky' at mid-morning, followed by dinner at mid-day, tea and supper. Supper would restore the cholesterol levels nicely with bread, butter and cheese during the summer, or hot bread and milk, with spoonfuls of sugar, on cold winter's nights.

All the farm workers had a 'docky bag' until about thirty-five years ago. It would contain great chunks of bread and cheese, raw onion and a flask of cold black tea. Two hours later they would cycle home for dinner. Sadly the 'docky bag' has almost disappeared – replaced by the coffee-break, complete with dainty tea-time biscuits. A corruption of the docky bag continues, for new villagers eating out at pizza parlours bring back 'doggy bags', full of leftovers, for their poodles or rottweilers.

Another word to have disappeared is the word to describe those workers with the fullest docky bags and the largest appetites. They were 'trenchermen' – derived from the old word 'trencher,' a large, flat wooden plate, round or square, on which meat was served. Consequently when enjoying our annual horkey, and my harvest breakfast, I keep the good rural tradition of 'trenchering' well and truly alive.

I keep another dietary tradition alive too. I still have dinner; a proper dinner, at the proper time of 12.30 p.m. or 1 o'clock. Sadly, these days 'dinner' seems to have been almost universally usurped by 'lunch'. When I was a boy the 'lunch break' at the village school was mid-morning, when we all had to reluctantly drink a third of a pint of ice-cold milk. Apart from that, lunch was eaten only by cricketers during test matches; evening 'dinner' was a luxury enjoyed by the privileged students at the nearby Cambridge colleges. According to the locals, dinner in the evening was only eaten by 'people who don't do no work', but who would probably have recognized a double negative when they heard one.

According to my Oxford Dictionary, 'dinner' is: 'The chief meal of the day, eaten originally, and still by many, about midday, but now, by the fashionable classes, in the evening.' I need stoking up at midday and I cannot see how the body can rest at night when it has to work digesting 'dinner'.

My vet has a theory: 'Dinner is dinner – the rest is fashion. Who would have believed it a few years ago – tattooed lorry drivers covered with oil going into a transport cafe and asking for croutons and moussaka. And where did all the paste go? They've all been to the Costa Brava now and come back calling it pâté.' He could be right; but I can write no more, it's half-past twelve and time for dinner.

131

41

Naf MAFF

I have a new problem, it is called the Ministry of Agriculture, Fisheries and Food. The CAP 'Explanatory Booklet' has just fallen through my letterbox and I understand hardly any of its 44 pages. I always thought that I was a simple countryman; in reality I must be a very thick, simple countryman. Paragraph 30 is typical of what I don't understand: 'The set-aside for 1992/93 is 15 per cent of the total of the area on which you are claiming area payments and the area set-aside under this scheme. For example, if you want to claim area payments on 85 hectares of eligible arable crops you must set-aside 15 hectares. You must remember to include the area you will be setting aside when calculating the 15 per cent. Do not simply take 15 per cent of the area you intend to crop. Appendix 2 explains in more detail how to calculate how much land to set-aside. [I don't understand Appendix 2 either.] The rules about set-aside are very strict in order to prevent fraud in all member states; you will lose some or all of your area payments if you do not set-aside enough land. It is important in your own interests to get this calculation right.'

The rules may be strict, but if you don't understand them, strictness becomes irrelevant. If anybody does understand the rules, then how does he apply for his set-aside money? That is easy – he can't, as no application forms have been printed yet, because 'certain of the rules are still subject to Parliamentary approval'. Brilliant. When the forms eventually arrive I think I will complete them in rods, poles, perches, roods and acres, to get my own back.

One section of the rules I do understand however; if set-aside is covered with weeds, or sown with grasses, it must be cut at least once before July 1st each year. If the option is 'bare summer fallow', the land must be cultivated before June 1st. This seems to be designed to ensure maximum carnage of young skylarks, lapwings, partridges, leverets and emerging butterflies. In addition 'bare summer fallow' will ensure a high population of the 'wheat bulb fly', so that when the field reverts to wheat, most of the seed will be eaten by the maggot of the wheat bulb fly, unless treated with chemicals – the fly needs bare soil during the summer to lay its eggs and can be a major pest. So MAFF has reached yet new and dizzy heights in its eco-illiteracy; I wonder if it employed a Greek olive grower on sabbatical as its cereals and wildlife adviser?

Another absurdity of the new compulsory set-aside scheme is that all those responsible farmers who have already taken land out of cereal production for environmentally friendly schemes such as the Countryside Stewardship Scheme, will be obliged to take still more land out of production – even if they have 15 per cent out already. It is totally unfair, but nothing new, as the environmentally aware farmer has been penalised by the system for the past 40 years – why should the MAFF bureaucrats change the habits of a lifetime?

It is strange that just as farm paperwork, rules and regulations are increasing, turning farmers into solicitors, economic forecasters, accountants, animal health consultants, landscape architects and so on, so farm incomes are planned to fall dramatically – a plan designed and encouraged by our beloved Members of Parliament. Yet these wonderful pillars of society, an example to us all, have just voted themselves a huge rise in their own expenses. They claim that their workload is increasing and they are having to act as solicitors, social workers and accountants – how sad. So why the difference between farmers and politicians?

Those voting for this selfish, inflationary rise make interesting

bedfellows – Edwina Currie, Teresa Gorman, Bernie Grant, Dennis Skinner, Uncle Tom Cobley and all. In case any scavenging libel lawyers read this I had better explain that the phrase 'bedfellows' is a harmless, colloquial expression, not, as far as I am aware, a statement of fact.

Last Sunday I made my way to the British Birdwatching Fair at Rutland Water, and bought two wonderful birdwatching toys. One is a loose metal stud in a small piece of wood, described as the Audubon Bird Call. When it is turned it squeaks and is supposed to attract birds, yet most of the birds in my garden fly away at great speed, as soon as the squeak joins in the dawn chorus. The other example of American hi-tech is a stick-on hawk outline to stop birds flying into my study window. They cost £5 each, but I paid up to help the ailing US economy.

Another birdwatching toy looked just the job; it was a baseball cap with a large microphone fitted vertically on top, connected to earphones; it was supposed to help birdwatchers hear birdsong. I resisted the temptation to buy my father one for his weekly visit to the Post Office to get his pension – it would have made him uncontrollable. Perhaps every MP should have one so they can pick up the howls of anguish as farmers read their CAP booklets.

42

The Great Huntingdonshire Chain-Saw Massacre

The telephone rang so early the other morning that even the larks were still sleeping. It was a farmer from the wilds of Huntingdonshire – a *Daily Telegraph* reader – complaining that a neighbouring farmer had spent all the previous day ripping out a hedge. Furthermore, he asserted that the grisly work would continue once the sun was up. 'Surely not,' I demurred, 'the NFU and nice Mr Gummer claim that farmers are the guardians of the countryside, and that such aberrations as hedgerow destruction died out years ago.' The good Huntingdonshire yeoman insisted that he was not hallucinating and would I come?

With my father riding shotgun, I ventured off the beaten track into the heart of old Huntingdonshire – John Major country. The farmer was pleased to see me: 'Good heavens, you're Mr Page are you? You look like a real farmer – I was expecting someone who would look more intellectual.' A back-handed compliment if ever I heard one.

Sure enough, at the end of a green lane the sorry work was still in progress. Three hundred yards of old hedgerow were being ripped out and heaped onto a fire, to make a big field even bigger. There is no sadder sight in the English countryside than the death of a hedge; twisted and shattered trunks and branches; shrivelled up leaves and silence – even the birds seem to know that their corridor of life is doomed. 'What does he want to do that for?' the farmer asked indignantly. It was a question that defied a logical, or a civil reply.

On my return home I phoned the offending farmer – an active NFU member. 'Oh', he said, 'I did wonder about the wisdom of getting rid of this – but I have no qualms about the other three.' I winced. 'You have to be efficient,' he went on, 'I have three farms around here and I'm afraid it has to be one farm one field these days.' I put the phone down slowly; it had been a very depressing morning.

It was ironic that this piece of destruction was actually going on during the launch of the RSPB's 'Campaign for the Countryside', in which the RSPB claimed that nearly 53,000 miles of hedgerow had been destroyed between 1984 and 1990. As sure as day follows night, so any conservation launch is followed by a statement from the NFU. It came, predictably, with the President of the NFU, Mr David Naish, claiming that 'farmers are determined to protect the countryside'. Mr Naish went on to criticize the RSPB: 'It is a pity that they should continue to use examples of what has happened in the past as a basis for castigating the way farmers are using their land.' I sometimes get the impression that the NFU is not actually talking about planet Earth. Perhaps it is Uranus that is still awash with woods, hedgerows and water meadows. If not, perhaps Mr Naish should visit Huntingdonshire – that would bring him down to real Earth with a real bump.

The other irony of the great Huntingdonshire Chainsaw Massacre is that it has taken place close to the home of the Prime Minister. Now John Major has said that he likes living in Huntingdonshire because he enjoys trees. Huntingdonshire has lost 90 per cent of its trees and hedgerows since the end of the Second World War – or, more accurately, 90 per cent plus three hundred yards. Who said Mr Major lacks a sense of humour?

Friends of mine, Mr Major's constituents, say that he is a very nice man, but they all have one criticism – he is a townsman from Brixton and simply does not understand the countryside. This is shown in the proposed sale of a beautiful old Cambridgeshire wood, again in Mr Major's constituency. It is a Site of Special Scientific Interest (SSSI) because of its age and the flora and fauna contained within it. For years it has been owned by the Ministry of Defence, with access for local people. Now it is surplus to requirements and instead of it being given to the Cambridgeshire Wildlife Trust, as common sense dictates, it is to be sold to the highest bidder, to conform with government policy. Presumably the money raised will buy half a spare tyre for a Hercules aircraft – or more port for the Officers' Mess.

With the woeful lack of country knowledge of Brixton Man, Mr Major says that Brampton Wood will be safe because it is an SSSI. Yet in the last two years over 500 SSSIs have been damaged, and within a couple of frog-hops from Brampton Wood a road is currently being built straight through the SSSI of Brampton Meadow. Already it is said that men with theodolites are eyeing up Brampton Wood for a slip road. Sadly, Mr Major's belief in the sanctity of the SSSI seems to be as sound as his conviction in the sanity of the ERM. Evidently the distance between Brixton and Brampton for Mr Major is as great as that between Uranus and Planet Earth for Mr Naish.

The day after the chainsaw trauma it was a relief to take the dog into one of our small fields, enclosed by a large, sprawling hedge; it will only be removed over my dead body. As I picked blackberries, a mob of blue tits, great tits and long-tailed tits were hurling insults at a little owl. The wild hedgerow harvest of fruit and berries is as good this year as the harvest of plums and apples in the orchard, with blackberries as big as raspberries, as well as hips, haws, crab apples, sloes, wild hops and the berries of spindle, buckthorn, elder, bryony and mountain ash. It was like walking back into old England, to catch a breath of beauty, sanity and reality. One farm, one field, indeed. I'm glad our one small farm has many fields – with beautiful hedges around every one.

43

Migrating from Maastricht

I really must smarten myself up; in my last diary I mentioned how I was informed that I looked like a 'real farmer'. Since then my appearance has evidently slipped, as I was invited to speak to a group of European peasant representatives, to coincide with a meeting of European Agricultural Ministers in Cambridge. As Mr Gummer and his guests were being punted down the River Cam, in all their evening finery, I was talking to a load of peasants – real peasants – in a Cambridgeshire barn.

By the end of the evening it seemed that not only did I look like a peasant, I was a peasant, for all of us there felt that Mr Gummer's 'CAP triumph' was in fact a disaster and that the main aim of EC agricultural policy is to get the small farmer, the peasant farmer and the family farmer, off the land. 'Small' is no longer beautiful, it is inconvenient – inconvenient to the politicians who now seem to believe that 'large' is wonderful; large is more easily controlled, managed and manipulated.

The gathering of peasants was arranged by an interesting environmental group, the SAFE Alliance, an alliance of organizations who want Sustainable Agriculture, Food and Environment. Sustainable agriculture is a simple wish made more remote by several aspects of the CAP reforms.

Ever since I can remember my village has been full of people with bird names. In one large house lived a Miss Raven, which made almost a complete set, as there was also a Rooke and my mother was a Crow, but sadly there were no Jackdaws. In addition there were Swans, Nightingales, Sparrows, Swallows, nearby there was a Finch and one old boy had the nickname of Linnet. Since then some bird names have flown the parish, but others have arrived;

Mr Partridge has come and gone, and a whole family of Goshawks have taken up residence.

It is odd how all these names are of birds and I cannot remember meeting anybody with an animal surname – never a Mr Rat or a family of Polecats. Of course there are plenty of animal nicknames: there is my old friend Badger Walker, as well as a long-departed local farmer known as Tup; I wonder how that name was acquired?

All this is a rather long-winded way of saying that the co-ordinator of SAFE is a very pleasant man by the name of Hugh Raven, who by coincidence is the nephew of the Miss Raven of my childhood. To most people all this is of no account, but it also transpires that Hugh Raven is the grandson of a childhood hero of mine, Canon C. E. Raven, a birdwatching vicar who wrote books about his travels and who became Master of Christ's College, Cambridge, between 1939 and 1950. Certainly his *In Praise of Birds* helped to inspire me as a boy.

Digging out my old copy of the book I have been reading it again with much pleasure – of the good Canon watching golden orioles nesting during the First World War, and of a pair of swallows nesting on the front line, in the thick of the fighting. The efforts of Canon Raven to get his swallows through a summer of war brings me to the problems and tensions of getting our third brood of swallows away now.

It is a mystery; after successfully rearing two broods in our barn with the special swallow roof, the birds suddenly switched to an old nest in the dairy. The hen bird did not start incubating until the middle of August and I was tempted to break the law and take the eggs away – to get two healthy parents away with two strong broods – but in the end we decided to let her sit. Four eggs hatched on time, after a fortnight, but a week later the first disaster struck – the nest crashed down, killing one youngster and leaving the other three homeless. I quickly nailed a small box to the wooden beam and put the surviving three young inside. Within two hours the parent birds were again feeding their chicks.

It then became clear that another disaster had struck. Only one adult remained – flying endlessly after insects as the weather cooled, in mist, sun and rain. What happened to its mate is unknown. Certainly, during the summer sparrowhawks made several attempts to get above the swallows to dive at them, perhaps on this occasion one was successful. More likely one of the auto-junkies, who race past the farm every day in their cars, ignoring the speed limit completely, smashed into the bird as it swooped low over the road.

Every day since, my eyes have turned upwards, looking for the faithful little bird working at its enormous task. Exactly on time,

139

on September 18th, the young birds left the nest. It was a day of relentless rain. I found one youngster, sodden, in a puddle. Its wing was damaged, so I returned it to the box. With two young on the wing and one in the nest the parent bird was at its limit. Several times the injured bird tried to fly, but fell again; it was getting thinner and slowly dying before my eyes. I put it out of its misery so that the parent could turn all its attention to the healthy two; it caused me much sadness as these late waifs had become my friends.

As I write the swallows are still here. The youngsters are flying strongly and, as always, the devoted adult is close by. I wish them well for their great autumn journey and hope to see them again next year. With good weather, and against the odds, they might just make it.

44

To Run and to Ride

Last September was an excellent month in the South West of England and on Exmoor in particular. 'The season of mists and mellow fruitfulness' had given warm still days and with it had come spectacular views of the moor and the sea.

I decided to go hunting – a day out with the Devon and Somerset Staghounds. I chose a special meet, the Memorial Meet for Sir Bernard Waley-Cohen at his old home of Honeymeade. Sir Bernard was a former chairman of the hunt and also a former lord mayor of London. It was meant to be a happy meet; to eat, drink, listen to a short tribute to Sir Bernard, and then off over some of the most attractive parts of the moor.

The day dawned, the weather broke and the rain came. It was not a gentle warm shower to match the season. The wind was cold and the rain blew in, falling like angled stair-rods, soaking, incessant and only a few degrees above ice.

In five hours the rain stopped for only twenty minutes. Every time I kicked my horse on, water squirted from the top of my boots in miniature fountains; I felt cold, damp and exposed – exposed because of my enormous horse – enormous to me, that was. As Bella had been unloaded from the horse-box, the words of Kevin, from the local stables, were not reassuring: 'Sorry Robin, I had forgotten you were so small.'

I had been before; in 1976 the cost of horse hire had been £22, in 1991, £75; in 2006 . . .? Cousin Fiona was in attendance, to pick me up in case my occasional and do-it-yourself horsemanship let me down. It did several times; my horse was so tall and my arms are so short that I had no chance of opening or closing gates; much to the wrath of those who could not see my predicament. In all my previous visits to Exmoor I had never seen it like this

141

– almost Exmoor under water. Amazingly, in the cold and wet, late swallows were still crossing the high ridges in small groups; I could not imagine them ever reaching Africa after such a soaking and buffeting.

But why was someone who claims not to hunt, riding with the Devon and Somerset Staghounds? The reason was simple; for years now, as an almost obsessive conservationist, hunting has intrigued me – the controversy of hunting, the misrepresentation surrounding hunting, the conservation value of hunting and the place hunting has in rural life. On top of all this, the form of hunting that arouses the most anger and controversy and reveals the most ignorance is staghunting. The 'antis' rail against it; newspapers normally sympathetic to the traditional countryside refuse to cover it, for fear of 'offending our readers'. Even some defensive foxhunters admit to 'drawing the line at staghunting'.

Yet staghunters continue to love their sport; it is carried out in some of the hardest and most spectacular hunting country in Britain, and without the interest of the hunters, the red deer of Exmoor would be under great threat from poachers, irate farmers and almost anybody with a gun. Those who take part in hunting also claim that staghunting is a humane way of killing deer; that the animal is shot at close range as it stands at bay, not 'torn to pieces' as suggested by some of those who deliberately misrepresent the sport.

I had returned to hunt on the moor for the fourth time in the hope of seeing a kill. It was not that I had developed an unquenchable blood lust, but I wanted to witness a kill so that I could judge for myself whether or not cruelty was involved. I also wanted to know what my emotional reaction would be.

I should have stayed at home, for yet again I saw no kill; hounds searched, found, lost and searched again. We galloped through the rain, mud flew, the sound of the huntsman's horn drifted in on the wind; we stopped, the horses steamed. Even in the torrential downpour the moor was beautiful.

Time for reflection ceased, hounds had 'found' again in the valley of the Exe – no longer a stream of clear water flowing musically to the sea, but a rushing, peat-stained torrent, rapidly rising into angry spate. Within minutes the stag had vanished again. Where? Scent had gone, huntsmen and hounds were puzzled, car followers were bemused. A false scent or a fine scent was followed into the valley of the White Water, but the stag had gone. For the fourth time there had been no kill; could a 'sport' in which nature so often won really be cruel?

Still it rained. Fiona's new, long 'Burghley' Barbour was now as wet inside as out; she looked far from nubile – more like a sack of saturated potatoes. It was not a good day for Barbour. We returned to base for a soaking of a more traditional kind. If there is anything more pleasant than lying in a hot bath after a hard, cold day's hunting, with a glass of whisky at hand, I have yet to discover it. And what about the next day? Warm and sunny of course.

But although I had still not seen a kill, I had seen the hunting culture of Exmoor and a brief glimpse of deer. For traditional Exmoor is a 'hunting culture', more sophisticated than those of the rain forest, or Arctic tundra, yet just as important and just as threatened. Exmoor's red deer herd now numbers about 2,000 animals and aproximately 170 are culled each year. It is a healthy and vigorous herd; its worst time was between 1825 and 1850 when hunting stopped. Without the protection of the hunt the deer were killed and poached and it was not until hunting resumed that deer numbers increased again.

Most of the moor's farmers like to see the deer. John Pugsley, who farms 1,300 acres, mostly as a tenant, is typical, although he prefers to hunt foxes to deer. He has many wild deer on his farm, but does not mind as long as damage is not too great and he gets the odd joint of venison. 'One of the most important factors in hunting', he says, 'is that it breaks up the large herds into little groups, and half a dozen deer are more acceptable than 60 or more. Those who criticize hunting seem unaware of this. Certainly if hunting stopped, deer pressure on my farm would become unacceptable and I would have to shoot. I believe they would be shot out in three years.'

In view of this, who are the people who want hunting banned and who would risk exterminating Exmoor's deer? There are two main groups. There are city dwellers who simply seem unable to understand the ways of the true countryside. They are opposed to hunting emotionally, as a reaction against 'the chase' and death. Politically they see it as the idle rich at play. It is true that some idle rich do hunt, but on Exmoor many of the hunters are local, without privilege, status or huge bank balances.

The other main group of opponents consists of middle-class incomers; one time holiday-makers attracted to retire to their summer utopia. They bring their civilized city standards with them; it would be utopia if it was not for the uncivilized rustics next door, round the corner and over the hill. Such people seem unable to realize that they moved quite freely into an area with its own distinctive traditions and culture. If they are offended by hunting, why not freely move off to a more acceptable area?

So, on Exmoor a culture is threatened by development, incomers and people uninterested in traditional ways. It is all incredibly sad, and one day, in the not too distant future, it is highly likely that Britain will become a plastic and nasty imitation of the real thing.

45

Wasted Wood Pulp

Two years ago, with much banging of drums, the government launched its fat environmental white paper, 'This Common Inheritance'. Its aim was to turn Britain into a green and pleasant land once more and save it from pollution, prairie farmers, developers and so on. Since then the huge tome has almost disappeared without trace – what a waste of wood pulp. However, the other day a small piece of positive conservation originating from the forgotten volume did reappear, with the launch of the Countryside Commission's Countryside Stewardship scheme.

In effect it is the next step on from farm set-aside. It will pay farmers who want to get involved with the restoration of heather moorland, heathland, cliff tops, water meadows and downland – it will be creative conservation at last. £13 million has been squeezed out of the Treasury for the scheme, of which £9 million will be available to farmers in the chosen areas.

At the time, the package appeared to be a feather in the cap of a buoyant Mr Heseltine – or at least he appeared to be buoyant, especially when compared to his drab and characterless Cabinet colleagues. But although the Countryside Stewardship Scheme is a positive step forward – what about the rest of Britain? Unfortunately the general countryside in which many of us live, is still being wrecked by concrete mixers, internal combustion engines and the reversible plough. When are farmers and land owners going to be encouraged to restore the ordinary country parishes of lowland England, and reward those farmers who have continued to farm responsibly?

Mr Heseltine said that more positive steps would follow; they do not seem to have followed very quickly. The truth is, that as farm incomes continue to drop, some big farmers, particularly in

Eastern England, are still becoming ever more intensive to try to maintain the third BMW. Hedges are still being ripped out, even during the nesting season for birds, and high input monoculture is still the order of the day.

The Countryside Commission's announcement was odd in many ways as it originated from the Department of the Environment and not the Ministry of Agriculture – although it was almost entirely about rewarding responsible and sympathetic farming. Where was Mr Gummer? An informant tells me that the Ministry of Agriculture was hardly consulted – most of MAFF's officials are very negative towards environmental initiatives and see their main work as controlling production, not safeguarding the countryside.

Indeed Mr Gummer's favourite word to describe British Farming is 'efficient'; he still has not grasped the fact that hedges, ponds, water meadows and woods, the very essence of the British countryside, reflect 'inefficient' but highly responsible farming. It is time that Mr Gummer called for responsible farming and 'efficient' government. Efficient government would be the absorption of the Ministry of Agriculture by the Department of the Environment. Logic suggests that environment and agriculture cannot, and should not, be treated as separate entities. Another advantage of a merger would be that Mr Gummer would then be demoted; this would allow him more time to indulge in his more saintly activities. It has long been my view that Mr Gummer is in the wrong job: I think he should have been a monk – preferably a Trappist one.

Sadly it seems that our current batch of MPs no longer understand the countryside or farming. Most of them originate from urban backgrounds and simply haven't a clue. One such urban Tory, representing a rural seat, was shown a new pond recently, created for wildlife. When told the pond contained newts he said: 'Oh yes, they are young frogs, aren't they?'

46

Autumn Ode

Life is proving very difficult at the moment; I have got things wrong. When I started writing over twenty years ago, part of the reason was to escape the trap of routine nine-to-five employment. I wanted to write when the urge took me and go for a walk when it did not. The only compromise was to work long, regular hours on the farm at harvest time. It was an enjoyable period. I hadn't got two halfpennies to rub together; few people wanted anything I wrote, yet I would watch fox cubs, look for butterflies and go searching for deer. I had time and I was extremely happy.

Now, with my father retired, I am needed more often on the farm and I am turning into a writing machine in order to finance various new projects. I suppose this comes from what the politicians would call the 'enterprise culture' in which we now live. The only problem is that I have very little enterprise and no culture.

My idyll is to have a kind benefactor who would allow me to do what I want to do most – to wander round the fields and hedgerows, writing the occasional pastoral essay and composing poems. My literary heroes are John Clare and W. H. Davies – I would love to write poetry like them. Early in the spring a poem did come to me, very early in the morning. It was wonderful, full of the sights and sounds of the British countryside. 'That's good,' I thought, 'I'll remember that and write it down when I get up.' Needless to say, after four more hours' sleep, I remembered nothing.

To overcome this problem I decided to sleep with pen and paper by my bed, so that the world would not miss another masterpiece. Sure enough inspiration came in the form of a poem that actually rhymed, about a cuckoo. I will not reproduce it here out of sheer embarrassment.

Then, last week another creation came out of the night. My

147

subconscious spurred me into action and I wrote it on automatic pilot, before collapsing back into sleep. Was it brilliant? Was it pastoral? Did it describe the wonders of the British countryside? When I awoke again at a civilized hour I read:

> Haze and smoke,
> The poison flows.
>
> Heat and dust,
> The ice is lost.
>
> Tide and flood,
> The land has gone.
>
> Nature dies,
> The world is quiet.
>
> Tears and pain,
> Cry for the earth.

I do apologise profusely to all those lovers of Clare and Davies – but that is how it came out. I suppose it reflects the state of my brain again. Incidently the 'poem' was entitled 'Economic Miracle'.

As if this was not enough, another 'poem' surfaced the next night in exactly the same way:

> The rain falls,
> The spring rises,
> The stream flows,
> The river winds,
> The sewage seeps,
> The acid burns,
> The poison bubbles.
> The fish die,
> The trees sigh,
> The dolphins weep,
> The gulls cry.
> The rain falls;
> The cycle of despair.

I suppose this little number should have been dedicated to water privatization. It was all becoming too depressing, so I removed the pen and paper from my bedside and have slept soundly ever since.

With the leaves turning and falling it has reminded me of midsummer when a wide area of dead leaves appeared in the beautiful old weeping willow tree close to the farmhouse. The strip of dead leaves went from the top of the tree to the bottom. Quite how this happened I do not know, although I suppose it could have been struck by lightning. As soon as the shrivelled leaves appeared, various itinerants began knocking on my father's back door wanting the job of cutting out the dead wood. They all had the same story: 'I'm a tree surgeon and spent years working for the Forestry Commission in Devon.' I suppose that if I had developed a headache the story would have been, 'I am a brain surgeon and I've been working for years for a hospital in Caithness.'

By now readers should have realized that my father gets much amusement out of life. Well, he remembers the fine old tree being planted. 'How old is it?' he asked the first forestry expert, with an air of genuine enquiry. The multi-talented scrap-merchant studied the willow carefully and informed him: 'It's at least 150 years old.' The second arboriculturist had a slightly different view: 'That tree's about 100 years old.' When a real tree surgeon arrived on the scene he estimated '50'; he was exactly right and got the job on the spot.

Normally I am opposed to cutting dead wood out of a tree, apart from when I'm logging, because it is needed for flourishing insect populations and for hole-nesting birds. The branches in this case, however, were almost directly over the footpath to my father's garage, so they had to go – if they had been over the garage itself and the old car inside, then that would have been a different matter.

47

Ill-Met By Moonlight

I usually enjoy the autumn, and as soon as the leaves begin to fall, and damp lingers on through the day, I visit a nearby wood, Hayley Wood. It is one of Britain's finest examples of ancient, coppiced woodland. However, unlike the assorted 'ologists' who flock to the area, I do not go seeking obscure fungi, plants or insects, I go to enjoy the sights and sounds of the rut; Hayley Wood is a traditional rutting area for the fallow deer.

As I entered the wood on my last visit I was disappointed. With the wind coming in from the west, the entrance to the wood was awash with one of the foulest smells I have ever had the misfortune to encounter. It almost matched the roadside sewers of India, and easily bettered the odour of my cricket socks after a hot summer day – it was coming from a nearby maggot factory.

How does a foul-smelling maggot factory, for the benefit of anglers, come to be sited next to one of the most important nature reserves in Cambridgeshire? The answer is simple: incredibly, South Cambridgeshire District Council gave the enterprise planning permission; it helps to show the superficial commitment to conservation of some planners.

To get away from the smell of decaying offal, I hurried to the far end of the wood. There the air was clean, but full of noise. The sky seemed to be overflowing with small planes, circling, climbing and diving, with one Tiger Moth even looping the loop.

Nearby there is a tiny airfield for small planes, and they all seemed to be lining up on the wood. This is a nature reserve – a nature reserve full of animal offal and various individuals demonstrating the mid-life Biggles syndrome. I could not believe it.

As darkness began to fall and the threat from the Luftwaffe faded, there was yet another interruption – barking. Had somebody lost a dog, again in a nature reserve? If so it was a very strange dog, giving a single loud bark, followed by a pause of four or five seconds, before another solitary bark. It went on and on.

Stalking the noise in the half-darkness was difficult, with every footstep rustling the drought-dry leaves. I looked but could see nothing, and still the barking went on. Suddenly a small shadow moved and fled. It was not a dog, but a muntjac deer – one of those attractive Asian escapees that have now colonized large parts of England south of the Wash. I had seen muntjac many times before in the wood, but had never heard the bark, which gives them their attractive alternative name of 'Barking Deer'.

It is strange how eyes and ears quickly attune themselves to a woodland dusk, helped by the light of a half-moon. Ahead I saw movement – a white fallow doe. The deer in the wood have almost a complete colour range from white to black. The white deer are the easiest to see. They are 'poachers' deer' for they betray the presence of the rest of the camouflaged herd. A good poacher, or stalker will always leave a white deer. Then came the sound I had been waiting for. The long deep groan of the fallow buck, followed by the short squeals of his cohorts.

The moon vanished behind clouds, and darkness was almost complete. A tawny owl called, and the buck continued his groaning of mastery and lust. I crawled closer, within a few yards. I could hear the hooves of the does among the leaves, and the pacing of their master. I left quietly, not wanting to cause fear. The fallow deer's new year had begun.

I felt happy and refreshed – until of course I waded once again into the air of the maggot farm's offal. I hope that next year the wind is from the east, and Biggles and his merry men are grounded.

48

Rolling Around

Rolling is one of the most enjoyable jobs on the farm. Once the winter wheat or oats have been sown the rolls give them a firm bed. Driving the tractor up and down the field is a soothing, satisfying occupation. Not only is it a good way of watching the ever-changing light on the autumn leaves, but it also allows time to think and dream.

As I was rolling the winter wheat the other afternoon a large flock of lapwings settled around me, the angle of the sun highlighting their silken green sheen. At one time lapwings nested each and every summer in the parish; now they are simply winter visitors – seasonal nomads searching for food and shelter.

It is strange to relate that probably the largest summer producers of lapwings are grouse moors, where, like the red grouse, the breeding lapwings are protected from predators by gamekeepers. Fox, magpie and crow are the main villains of the piece.

Now the League Against Cruel Sports is running a campaign against predator control. It is almost beyond belief. With no protection it would mean that our winter lapwings would disappear too. One more loss contributing towards the day when a winter landscape becomes an empty landscape.

It baffles me how many of these often well-meaning antis simply fail to understand the mechanisms that keep the countryside alive. Must the RSPB cease predator control to protect avocets? Must various wildlife trusts cease predator control to protect terns? If not, then why should similar protection be denied to grouse, and to the lapwings, curlews, golden plovers, dunlins, merlins and redshanks that share the high heather moors with them during the breeding season?

*　　*　　*

A hazard in rolling our largest field is that one side is made up of heavy clay. As I was still musing about lapwings, the front wheels hit a solid clod, which catapulted me roofwards. It broke my train of thought and for some inexplicable reason when I landed I was thinking of Mr Gummer.

I went to the Conservative Party Conference this year, hoping to be called to the rostrum during the agriculture debate. I am an old-fashioned traditional Tory, not one of the modern breed of Born Again Cash-Flow Tories whose main aim seems to be profit, usually their own. I suspect however, that after recent articles in this column about disappearing hedgerows, and so on, the party managers made sure that I was kept well away from the microphone. Instead, the speakers from the floor heaped praise on Mr Gummer – one for the second year running, in song. It was excruciating. All this allowed Mr Gummer to give a speech, not in defence of his ill-conceived CAP reforms, but in praise of Europe.

I have to confess that I am gaining more respect for Mr Gummer. He is a good speaker, he fights his corner and he does seem to be gaining a better grasp of farming and the environment; sadly his European straitjacket and his inability to appreciate the difference between 'efficient' farming and environmentally friendly farming, means that he does still have some way to go.

What I had hoped to tell Mr Gummer publicly was quite simple. His CAP agreement is based on 15 per cent set-aside; it is now clear that this means that the clever farmer and the hooligan farmer will simply take out of production their worst land and add more chemicals to the rest – so production will remain the same and the whole purpose of set-aside will be defeated. At the same time an increasing number of hedgerows are being ripped out and marginal land is being brought into production to make up for the lost 15 per cent. Since reporting the ripped-out hedgerow in Huntingdonshire a month ago, I have seen several more, in a number of counties.

Even worse, in a neighbouring village, a chalk quarry, famous for its orchids and chalkland wildflowers has been partially filled in and planted with cereals. The cereal grower/land manager (in my view he can't be called a farmer) was even offered annual Stewardship payments to leave it alone, but no, the bulldozer went in – all thanks to set-aside, it seems.

Nitrogen quotas were the simple and obvious way to reduce production. Strangely Mr Gummer says that these would infringe upon a farmer's individual freedom – just like set-aside and quotas.

Being a glutton for punishment, while at Brighton, I also heard Michael Howard, the Secretary of State for the Environment, and his dreadful underling, David MacLean. One old farmer was not impressed by what he heard: 'They're just right for the environment', he said, 'Howard is so wet he's almost liquid and MacLean is so lightweight he's almost airborne.' On the evidence available it was hard to disagree.

MacLean seemed to suggest that all environmental campaigners are extremists and that SSSIs, including Twyford Down, must not be allowed to hinder 'development'. I think he needs a few hours rolling on my tractor; it might help him to get a fraction closer to reality.

49

Hen-Pecked and Harried

My old father has become hen-pecked. It has nothing to do with the fact that he has been married for 55 years; indeed he started courting when he was 13 and my mother was 12, making a total of 64 happy years. No, he actually keeps getting pecked by hens. Last Wednesday after collecting the eggs he arrived in the farmhouse looking like the creature from the black lagoon, with his left eye streaming with blood.

As he had looked into the nest box the hen had looked out, and the hen won the confrontation. It is the third time in two years that he has been savaged by a hen in this way. The wound looked dreadful but fortunately no permanent damage was done. I hope Edwina Currie does not hear about this horror in the henhouse, otherwise the House of Commons will demand that we test Father for salmonella, with a giant swab every three months, just like the hens. I think for safety's sake I will persuade him to collect the eggs wearing my cricket helmet, complete with face guard. If things get any worse perhaps he should wear gloves, pads and box as well.

It is a sad fact that hens are not the brightest of God's creatures. This year we had a feathery Cochin hen which went broody in a double nestbox. She would leave her clutch to feed, and on returning she would invariably jump back into the empty side, where she would happily sit on nothing until picked up bodily and moved back to her eggs. Now this lunatic hen has been joined by a demented goose that has just started to lay – in the autumn. All very strange.

Following my recent Diary comments about families with bird names, several people have been kind enough to tell me about a sizeable chunk of the population with animal names, as well as several families – sorry shoals – of Haddocks and Herrings. There are Bucks, Does, Foxes, Bulls and Rabbittes. In Suffolk and St Neots there are large numbers of Squirrels, while in Ireland, in almost biblical tranquillity, there was once a Mr Wolfe living next door to a Miss Lamb.

My lambs have just gone off to market. I have been putting off the day for some time as I like my sheep. I am not getting sentimental in my old age, but nearly all the slaughter houses have closed down in the area, thanks to ridiculous EC regulations. In addition, Cambridge Cattle Market, just four miles away, has ceased operating, which means that our animals now have to be carted long distances to an abattoir, with a lengthy stop at Bury St Edmunds market, mid-journey.

As a result our beasts are being moved and messed about all day, and sometimes even longer, which to us is unacceptable. Fortunately we have now discovered a genuine farmers' co-operative locally, the Anglia Quality Meat Association Ltd. It arranges the sale of livestock directly to slaughterhouses for some 300 members, which cuts out time, stress and discomfort for the animals. It means that my conscience is now almost clear; it will be completely clear if and when mobile slaughterhouses become the norm.

Our sheep have had a better deal than many British sheep. A farmer recently told me of a trade centred in Wales that takes thousands of live sheep to Italy. Before being loaded up, the sheep are sheared, even in mid-winter, so that still more can be crammed into the lorries. Such a practice and such a journey fill me with anger and disgust.

Going to check my ewes at the weekend I screeched to a halt outside a friend's house on spotting their Metro, minus two wheels. Thieves had visited their quiet backwater and stolen the wheels during the night, kindly leaving two piles of bricks in their place. Steve had then climbed into the car and driven it off the bricks in spectacular fashion. There must be something about Metros. A few years ago a woman called at the farm to ask if we could pull her Metro out of a muddy field gateway. My brother got the tractor out; fixed a rope to the stranded vehicle and proceeded to pull its back wheels off. That was quite spectacular too.

It is with fear and trepidation that I again mention the dreadful BBC television programme, 'Countryfile'. Last time I criticized it my answerphone worked overtime for weeks; as soon as the programme ended each Sunday it filled up with complaints, ridicule and dissatisfaction – all totally justified in my view. I wish those who find the wasted half hour as irritating as I do, would complain to the BBC and not me.

However, I have found two viewers who love Countryfile; they are the Controller of BBC 1, Jonathan Powell and Countryfile's Editor, Tim Manning. They both think it is wonderful; so the programme has viewing figures of at least two, although it has to be said that neither of them is a countryman, and of course Jonathan Powell even likes Eldorado. Tim Manning has taken me to task for publicly 'trashing' Countryfile; I find the word 'trashing' an awful Americanism – I expect we will hear it on Countryfile soon. The fact that the programme regularly and publicly 'trashes' people who can't answer back seems to have escaped him.

Now one of my Countryfile moles tells me that the programme is looking for a black presenter – which presumably will gain Mr Manning a few more Brownie points from the BBC's trendy hierarchy.* To be fair to all ethnic, religious and sexual minorities, how about a Hindu Scottish crofter fronting The Money Programme; a gay disabled dolphin being trained to take over from David Attenborough and a New Age Eskimo reading the winter weather forecast?

* By early 1993 Countryfile was using a charming black presenter. Sadly I could see no sign of any charming country bumpkin, man, woman or 'person'.

50

Ram-Raider

I have suddenly become a great follower of proverbs; I have always enjoyed them, but now I am a believer – particularly in the one which claims 'He that laughs last, laughs longest.'

Recently, it will be remembered that friends of mine had two wheels stolen from their Metro, while it was parked outside their house. I thought it was a huge joke and generously shared their misfortune with all and sundry. This was before I parked my car at Royston Station in order to make one of my rare and fleeting visits to the Black Hole of London. It was obviously folly to travel by British Rail. At Royston Station, British Rail has the interesting policy of removing money from customers for the privilege of parking and using their trains, while offering virtually no security or service in return.

Consequently, when I returned from London I discovered that not only had I lost two wheels, I had lost the other two as well. This in itself would not have been a great loss, but unfortunately the missing wheels were still attached to the rest of the car. Yes, some unscrupulous swine had stolen my beloved Daihatsu Fourtrak in its entirety. At least my loss was shared. The next day I was due to pick up a ram for my ewes – not Eric this year but Tom. Now they would have to wait.

The policewoman on the phone sighed: 'Oh, another Fourtrak – they're very popular with thieves at the moment.' So, it transpires, are virtually all the cars parked in British Rail carparks. I wonder why Commercial Union Assurance, my insurance company, did not warn me that my car was at extra risk? I suppose they like the easy life of sitting on their backsides, paying out claims and increasing premiums.

A kind policeman called to take a statement 'and would you like a visit from the Victims of Crime Support Group?' What a strange world; it was only a car, but already I was a 'victim of crime' and somebody wanted to come and dry my eyes with hand-held Kleenex. The only visit I wanted was from the criminals themselves – yes, my front-door key was under the driver's mat of my car – so that I could test the sights of my .22 rifle.

Of course I did not expect sympathy from Linda and Steve, the Metro owners. But what did I get? Not simple laughter, no, they literally rolled around the floor with uncontrollable mirth – that's friendship for you.

The next day two friends from Malawi called. Being good trenchermen (one is actually a trencherwoman), I took them in my father's car – a heap of motorized rust that nobody in their right mind would steal – over the hill to the Royal Oak, for a proper mid-day 'dinner'. Just as I was about to go through the door I gulped, and then let out what I can only describe as an exclamation of indignation – as my own car, complete with its fifteen stickers in the back window, drove past.

I ran back to my father's wreck and set off in hot pursuit, leaving my friends abandoned and bewildered. Copying the gentlemanly driving skills of Ayrton Senna, I overtook a bus at speed, on a corner; caused an oncoming cyclist to swerve into a roadside heap of sugarbeet as an act of self-preservation, then cut up a pensioner out for a quiet spin in the country, probably causing his pacemaker to go into reverse.

At the next village of turnings, lanes and drifts I lost track of my car, and so still seething, I returned to the Royal Oak; passing a strange cyclist covered in mud and sugarbeet leaves as I went.

In great indignation I phoned the police: 'Oh,' said the voice at the other end, 'you've come through to the wrong department.' I am afraid that at that point I let out another exclamation of indignation – closely followed by one more as 'Robin!' my friends shouted, 'your Fourtrak has just driven past again.' It was getting rather like Laurel and Hardy. Half an hour later, when we were well and truly entrenched in the apple pie, a police panda car drove slowly by. Sadly I had a South Cambs District Council meeting to attend that afternoon and so could not visit all the local didecoys' camps, where my car would almost certainly have been found. Why the police did not swamp the area is a mystery, particularly as my vehicle is so distinctive with its stickers – No Referendum. No Ratification – taking pride of place.

That night at 11.30 the telephone rang while I was still slaving away for the *Daily Telegraph*. It was the police, my car had been found at a nearby garage – what a relief. Oh dear, I had reacted too early; it had not been left parked in the forecourt, but in the garage shop, next to the counter. My beautiful, innocent, gentle Daihatsu had become a successful ram-raider.

I arrived at the garage shop to see it surrounded by broken glass, bent and scratched, having been driven through a large window. 'With parking like that', I said, 'you must be looking for a woman.' 'No sir', the officer replied, 'a woman would have missed.' (Please no letters from feminists – we were trying to joke.)

'Why didn't you flood the area and get them this afternoon?' I asked the attendant policeman.

'It's nice that you've kept your sense of humour sir,' the officer replied. 'Flood? We've got three panda cars at best, for over 120 villages.' At that density criminals have more chance of being run over by a bus than being caught. Perhaps I should try ram-raiding instead of farming; it must be very exciting and it seems to pay. It is also good to know that the people concerned are not lying in bed all day; they are out and about at all hours, happy, active and using their intitiative. They may even be government agents, knocking down walls, crashing through windows and bending Daihatsus as part of a secret work creation scheme.

Apparently the night before, my Daihatsu 'Ram Raider' had been involved in a robbery at a building society in which over £20,000, plus the cash dispenser, was stolen in St Ives (Cambs). A nearby publican saw the crime in progress and called the police. It took the criminals over seven more minutes to lift the money, with the police arriving only after the crooks had vanished. The moral of this story is simple, if you are likely to be raped, kidnapped, mugged, or murdered, then do not visit Cambridgeshire, unless you ask the criminals to work extremely slowly.

The crooks had stolen all my cassettes, except 'Conservation in Profitable Farming' produced by Ciba-Geigy. This seems to suggest that the criminals might also work for the Ministry of Agriculture. They also kindly stole just one cricket boot; this could cause me great problems next season.

The ram-raiders had gained access to my Fourtrak by ripping out the door lock with a screwdriver; the ignition had gone the same way and then the screwdriver had been pushed down the hole, turned and bingo. All this means that my own current car key is a screwdriver.

Two days later, with the steering wheel chained to the driver's seat I again left my car at Royston Station. This time the parking ticket machine did not work. Arriving back from the Black Hole at 11.45 p.m. after enjoying *Country Living*'s annual party, I was relieved to see that my car was still there – but wait a minute, it had gained something – yes, an attractive yellow wheel clamp. Thankyou British Rail, I am sorry that we customers are such an inconvenience to you.

Next morning, £30 lighter, my car was free, or was it? I had my car keys, but I had forgotten my screwdriver . . .

Yes, my mind is made up. I am going to become a ram-raider and I am going to start by ramming British Rail at Royston. In fact I have made one ram-raid already, as Tom has now been taken to the ewes, who seem highly delighted.

My new year's resolution is simple: never again will I laugh at somebody else's misfortune.

51

Encounter

We had a visitor to the farm the other day. In the animal yard I came across a young leather-jacketed youth looking at our two Middle White gilts, Snowdrop II and Crocus. A gilt is a young lady pig, no longer a piglet, but not yet a sow; in my part of Cambridgeshire we pronounce gilt as 'yilt' – a strange piece of dialect as we do not call goats, yoats. The young man was obviously a thinker: 'I'm a vegetarian,' he told me, 'I don't believe in keeping animals shut up.' It was foggy, cold and damp; the two gilts were gazing at the thinker while lying snugly in clean, deep, warm straw; they were not impressed by what they heard. 'You mean we should have our animals outside, free-range?' I asked. He looked puzzled. 'What?' I explained that on our cold, heavy clay the animals were better off indoors. This time he was the one not impressed; meat eating was wrong and his diet consisted of delicious soya burgers, nut cutlets and bean sprouts. When I told him that I was worried by soya production, he looked as if his brain had decided to go on holiday. 'What?' he grunted, totally baffled. I explained that soya growing meant introducing a chemical based monoculture to the third world and also that some of the soya fields were on land cleared of rain forest. His reaction was inspired: 'What?'

When I asked him why he was wearing a leather jacket when he was a vegetarian, his answer came as a complete surprise. 'What?' he spluttered. He was a political studies student from a local college and was 'into animal rights'. From the number of times he said 'what', I had expected him to be a trainee electrician.

I explained crop rotations and how animals give us manure for the land and why I eat meat; it all seemed new to him. As he left, he turned to wave goodbye – too late, before I could shout a warning,

he had walked into a heap of something quite unpleasant. 'Never mind', I sympathized, 'it is organic.'

The animal on the farm that lives the most comfortable life is the donkey, Brinny. In bad weather she is content to stay in her stable, dry and out of the wind; when the weather improves she brays until she is let out. In addition, every morning she starts the day with a cup of tea. Her liking for tea was discovered when she developed laminitis (an unpleasant horsey ailment). She went off all her food and drink, until my sister tempted her with tea, served in a large, rose decorated mug. She sniffed it, tasted it, and has been an enthusiastic tea drinker ever since. On one occasion, to hasten recovery, two teaspoonfuls of sugar were added; it was a mistake, since then she will only drink sweetened tea. Every morning she has to have her steaming mug of tea and the mug is used exclusively for Brinny – exclusively, that is, except when the VAT man calls.

Last year a rather large lady visited the farm and demonstrated the even larger gap that has developed between town and country. On seeing a cow she asked: 'Is that a donkey?' To this day I do not understand how anybody could confuse a cow with a donkey. However, if the donkey had asked: 'Is that a woman?' I would have understood completely.

163

52

Politicians and Pigs

A sleek ministerial looking car swept into the farmyard the other day and a sleek ministerial looking man got out. Yes, that's right, John Gummer visited Bird's Farm – please don't faint – and we both survived the experience. I had simply written to the Secretary of State for Agriculture requesting a visit, as I wanted to ensure that he fully appreciated the plight of the ordinary, small, family farm. We had crossed swords, in a gentlemanly fashion, at a fringe meeting at the Conservative Party conference and I wanted to continue the discussion, with some practical examples. Fortunately, Mr Gummer was already due to visit Cambridgeshire, and he was able to include us in his schedule.

For some time too I have been worried by his use of the word 'efficient', as in 'efficient farming'. Hedges, wildflowers, butterflies, kingfishers and barn owls could all be said to be signs of inefficient

farming by the monoculture barley barons – the high priests of efficient farming. Consequently I wanted to show Mr Gummer environmentally friendly farming; farming that tries to rear animals humanely, produce good food and make a profit, while respecting wildlife and traditional landscapes.

Only three concessions were made for the Minister; my father was told that on no account was he to mention the Church of England (he is a life-long Baptist), Maastricht, or the wages of politicians; I took the seat cover off the passenger seat of my car so that Mr Gummer's suit did not become covered with mud, dog hair, feathers, hay and sheep meal, and Mr Gummer was offered coffee, scones and cake. Alas, he was too full to eat the cake, which has already entered into the folklore of the farm as 'Gummer cake'. Next summer, in the farm shop, the sales patter will describe it as 'cake almost eaten by Mr Gummer'. I should also make it clear that Mr Gummer's coffee was served in a clean cup – not the large mug reserved for the donkey and the VAT man.

My father cut a fine figure in his old coat and wellington boots, one green and one black. The Secretary of State was obviously impressed by his sartorial elegance, especially the boots: 'I expect you've got another pair like that', he said with a smile; sadly not, the other boots have leaks.

My mother was most impressed. Her frequent cry is: 'Mr Gummer is a nice man – he does his best; you shouldn't keep writing all those things about him.' Well, I have to say that I was impressed too; Mr Gummer listened, laughed and we had a 'vigorous exchange of views'.

And what did we talk about? After all, it is not every day that you get the opportunity to harangue a minister for an hour and a half. When Mrs Thatcher was elected to power in 1979 she promised that there would be an end to the 'nanny state'. Since then we have become weighed down by nannies – European nannies, national nannies and local government nannies. I told Mr Gummer about the problems they created and he seemed to be as irritated by them as we are.

For instance, at the Government's suggestion we 'diversified' some time ago. We opened the farm up to the public, and schools in particular, to gain an extra income. To guide visitors to the farm we obtained planning permission for twelve temporary RAC signs at a cost of £150. Now the county council refuses to renew planning permission for the signs; it is demanding permanent county council signs at £600 each. This we cannot afford; so now we have no signs. Visitor numbers, and income, have fallen as a direct result.

Cambridgeshire County Council says that we must have permanent signs to conform with its 'tourism policy'; apparently national agricultural policy is of no account. Gummer was not impressed. I gave him a list involving eleven similar nannies.

Another problem I outlined was the lack of a long-term, fully integrated rural policy, taking into consideration conservation, preservation, rural employment and the maintenance of thriving country communities and commercial farming. One way to contribute to all these things would be for more money to flow into the countryside for environment-friendly farming, paid for by the consumer.

Cheap food often means environment-unfriendly farming, and so the consumer, demanding cheap food, must accept some of the responsibility for the protection of wildlife and landscape on farmed land. The revenue, I suggested, could be obtained by a 2 per cent environmental tax on food. This would yield more than £837 million and add only 0.25 per cent to inflation.

Considering that the amount of money available for the new environment-friendly Stewardship Scheme is just £30 million over three years, such an environmental tax could breathe new life into the countryside, creating jobs, allowing less intensive agriculture and securing our wildlife and our landscapes for the future.

Gummer was not dismissive. He admitted that a good case could be made for an environmental tax on consumers and he looked most thoughtful.

After that, he went on to meet Cowslip the Jersey house cow; Crocus the Middle White pig; he saw our largest sprawling hedge and liked it and he was shown some of Cambridgeshire's most bleak prairie land. As I have mentioned, last year we had a woman visit the farm who did not know the difference between a cow and the donkey. Not only did Mr Gummer know the difference, but he also knew that the beef cows were Murray Greys. Unfortunately a photographer snapped Mr Gummer talking to the donkey. The picture appeared in *Farmers Weekly* with the caption, 'John Gummer tells a rapt audience about his plans for agriculture.'

Actually the Minister seemed to be almost on the environmental side and like me professed to hate the modern trend of neat and tidy farms and farmland, that seem almost sterile and homogenized.

So, if Mr Gummer seems well informed and environmentally aware, why do so many of the sounds coming from his Ministry seem the exact opposite? I suppose it could be the 'Yes Minister' syndrome; the right minister, but the wrong, negative civil servants, always explaining why new, positive, eco-literate policies cannot be implemented.

As Mr Gummer swept out of the farmyard in his sleek, ministerial car, I was pleased he had come. I liked him. In fact I only had one regret – that I had not let my father loose on the subject of Maastricht. It could have changed the course of history.

53

Global Yawning

Mr Heseltine has been a very busy man lately. For those of us who live in areas that are rapidly disappearing under bricks and mortar, one of his statements was not welcome. The former Secretary of State for the Environment expressed delight that an increase in the number of new houses being built indicated that the recession was on the way out.

What an extraordinary way to measure the depth of a recession – house building activity. Does this mean that a Government anxious to speed up economic growth will encourage new building regardless of planning considerations? Certainly numerous cases have come to my attention recently of developers running rings around planning authorities. When plans are refused the developers simply appeal, often giving the planning Inspectors totally bogus information, and almost invariably they win on appeal – green belt land, conservation areas, they all disappear under an assortment of architectural abortions. So, I think an important question should be answered by Mr Heseltine: have the liberal views of the Planning Inspectorate resulted from a definite government policy to build its way out of recession? I would rather have a recession than the planning mayhem that is currently taking place in East Anglia.

Last year Mr Heseltine launched a publicity campaign to help counter global warming. The campaign slogan was 'Helping the Earth Begins at Home'. Mr Heseltine and the Energy Secretary wanted people to use domestic energy more sparingly, to reduce carbon dioxide emissions and so reduce 'global warming'.

Sadly the campaign was only being allocated £10 million, whereas hundreds of millions of pounds are being spent annually persuading us to use more petrol, oil, coal and electricity. So the car, coal and oil industries win hands down and global warming will accelerate. In reality the politicians consider the jobs and taxes created by the car economy too important to be tampered with, regardless of global warming. Short term political and economic aims are considered to be far more vital than the survival of the planet.

Of course some flat-earth MPs still believe that global warming due to pollution is not taking place. One of these seems to be the extraordinary Conservative MP for Billericay, Mrs Teresa Gorman. Mrs Gorman recently won substantial libel damages after a member of her constituency party misrepresented her. Mrs Gorman felt aggrieved. Now, using her 'parliamentary privilege', Mrs Gorman, fighter for truth and justice, has called Mr Jonathan Porritt and Sir James Goldsmith 'eco-terrorists talking mumbo jumbo'. Her reason for this seems to be that they regard global warming as a reality. Now I happen to know Jonathan Porritt. He is a mild mannered, reasonable, pleasant man who says what he believes in a considered way – surely this does not make him any kind of terrorist?

In her Commons speech – sorry, tirade – Mrs Gorman also accused some environmentalists of being socialist sympathizers: 'Many of them are ex-socialists now wearing green wellies but with red linings still.' I have been a paid-up member of the Tory Party since my teens and my boots have been green ever since I can remember – certainly for 25 years before I had ever heard of the extraordinary Mrs Gorman. I believe that global warming is an alarming reality and all the hot air from the member for Billericay will not change my view.

Over the years one Tory Minister has repeatedly worried me. Privately, my good friend John Gummer is a pleasant, amusing man. Publicly he often seems rather small-minded, a man without vision, toddling along in the shadow of the NFU and the prairie farmers of his Suffolk constituency.

At last, he has done something sensible and positive – he has announced the phasing out of drift-netting off the Northumberland coast. He has not put a timetable on this move, but at least it is a step in the right direction. For years it has been known that the drift-netters of the North East have been taking substantial numbers of Atlantic salmon returning to Scottish rivers to breed. The salmon is one of Britain's most remarkable and beautiful wild creatures and it needs this helping hand as numbers continue to plummet. So well done Mr Gummer – better late than never.

Almost inevitably of course, Mr Gummer's action has been criticized. The National Federation of Fishermen's Organizations has condemned the move, claiming that it will put men out of work and that Mr Gummer is pandering to the whims of Scottish landowners. Most fishermen also claim to be conservationists; by their apparent disregard for the long term future of the salmon, perhaps the vociferous members of the National Federation of Fishermen's Organizations should tell us what they mean by 'conservation'.

54

A Boaring Tale

I am glad Mr Gummer enjoyed meeting Crocus the Middle White pig when he visited the farm the other day. Middle Whites are friendly, good natured pigs; unfortunately for them, although they are an old, traditional breed, they are also, in modern-day parlance, apple sauce compatible.

Mr Gummer met Roger as well, a neighbour's boar on a working holiday at Bird's Farm, making his name most appropriate. Roger has an interesting history; his mother was Lily the pig, owned by Fiona Silver, whose beautiful pictures once accompanied my articles and books, before she disappeared into the outback of Australia.

Lily's mother had no milk and so a local farmer was going to knock the unfortunate Lily on the head. Fiona, recognizing a real character, hand reared the poor, starving little object until Lily became a lively, squealing, normal piglet, with all the charming attributes of a Large White/Landrace cross.

As soon as Lily was mobile, another disaster struck: Sam the dog decided he would try a bit of live pork chop – almost detaching Lily's head and one leg from her shoulders. Because of the urgency of the situation the piglet was sown up with fishing line, using a hypodermic needle, on the kitchen table. Not only did she survive, she flourished, becoming a local celebrity and friend of all the children as they went to school. Then, after a brief liaison with a young Welsh boar called LLewellyn, Roger and various brothers and sisters came into the world.

This potted history of Roger's ancestry demonstrates that he comes from resilient stock, which was shown when the time came to put him in the trailer to take him back to his home. His attachment to Crocus was so great that instead of walking up the ramp and into the trailer, he burst through a hurdle and proceeded to climb up the haystack next to the sty containing his friend. What do you do when a pig goes climbing? Shout 'sit'? Throw him some Kendal Mint Cake? Give him a membership form for the Ramblers' Association? Or shout out the name of the nearest butcher's shop? Before I had made up my mind, Roger took the decision for me. From a height of 8 feet he jumped back into the sty, doing a graceful double somersault as he went, before landing squarely on his head; for the first time in my life I had seen a pig fly. He bounced, shook himself and carried on as if nothing had happened. If it had been the springboard diving event at the pig Olympics, Roger would have been awarded nine out of ten for content and one out of ten for presentation.

Thinking of pigs reminds me of Phil Drabble, not in any derogatory way, but because Phil has two piglike qualities that he shares with me. He likes good food and he enjoys rootling about in woods. Both came together at a recent award ceremony when Phil Drabble received a Centre of Excellence Award from the Forestry Authority for his outstanding conservation work at his home, Goat Lodge, and for his co-operation with the managers of adjoining Forestry Commission land. In the same way as a gamekeeper provides a surplus of pheasants, Phil has created a surplus of wildlife to spill over into the surrounding countryside.

Unfortunately his methods have been too successful and a surplus of sparrowhawks has almost wiped out Phil's beloved ornamental ptarmigan pigeons. More about the growing menace of sparrowhawks another time.

Phil has made his land, which has become an SSSI, into an Educational Nature Reserve, for the use of the local village First School. I hope the next door Forestry Commission land is not privatized, for it could put all Phil's work and vision in jeopardy.

The most enjoyable part of the bun fight came when a forestry man announced: 'The award ceremony will now take place 200 metres along the road.' 'Metres,' interrupted Phil, 'it's 200 yards up the road – we're English.' My feelings exactly – metres, grams and litres remain totally foreign to me, and I hope they always will.

Normally on Boxing Day I go to the local meet of the Cambridgeshire Foxhounds, to show solidarity with those out riding and to demonstrate support for my country heritage and traditions. This year however, I have a choice of sports and have chosen the blood sport in which the blood and violence will be most obvious. Yes, I am going to the local football derby between Cambridge United and

Peterborough; those with a fragile disposition should go to watch the foxhounds.

Last year my nephew wanted to go to the meet, but his pleasant wife, from an urban background, disapproved. Female chauvinism won and he stayed at home. The next day Andrew and Tracy walked around the farm with me and Bramble. On the set-aside, a hare got up and Bramble was off: with a slight feint the hare sent Bramble one way while it went the other. Not to be outdone, Bramble turned on a sixpence and ran like the wind, gradually closing the large gap. At the end of the field the hare whipped round at 90 degrees, found two more gears and accelerated away. Bramble gave up. Tracy was bubbling: 'That was exciting', she enthused. 'Yes it was', I replied, 'and you know what you have just been watching – hare coursing.' The learning process in the countryside is an interesting one.

55

Ding-Dong Merrily Below

Although I can't sing, I do enjoy carol-singing and always have. 'Silent Night', 'The Holly and the Ivy', 'O Little Town of Bethlehem' – I love them all. Indeed, I like 'In the Bleak Mid-Winter' so much that I want it sung at my funeral, even if that falls in the middle of a heatwave during July.

In the past I have sung carols off-key for so long, and at such volume, that by the time Christmas Day arrived I had developed a sore throat and lost my voice. I did not mind, of course, it was a good excuse to sample the ginger wine and sloe gin.

My love of carols started at the village school. During the nativity play, as Mary cradled the infant Jesus, or stumbled across the stage carrying him by his head, we shepherds would be belting out: 'While Shepherds Watched'. The school also had a link with King's College, Cambridge, and one year we all went to a rehearsal of their famous carol service – sitting right next to the choir. The King's Festival of Nine Lessons and Carols remains a delight, and I never miss listening to it on the radio on Christmas Eve, sometimes covered in down as we pluck the last of the cockerels.

Then there was carol-singing around the village with members of the Baptist Chapel. It would take two nights to do the rounds – stopping frequently to sing a whole carol or even two. It was like a scene from Thomas Hardy's *Under the Greenwood Tree*, with lanterns for light and clothing piled on in many layers to keep out the cold.

In the early days, old Mr Carter would accompany the singing with his violin. He had learned to play at the Scalded-Cat School of Music, but fortunately the singing normally drowned the screams and screeches scraped out on his ancient instrument. He was a kind and gentle man, and after every rendering, as our ears recovered, he would give a great toothless smile. To end the first night's singing we would have hot mince pies and coffee in the home of a wise old countrywoman. She knew the Latin names of all the wildflowers, studied ancient leather-bound herbals and could recite poetry to suit every turn of conversation.

Gradually, as the pace of life quickened, so did the carol-singing. To match the changing cashflow economy, it became cashflow carol-singing, rushing around the whole village in a single night. A verse here, a snatch of 'We Three Kings' there, a rattle of the collecting tins and away.

I did not like this new, high-speed version of an old tradition; neither my vocal chords, nor my legs could cope, and so one year I stopped. Others too, could not stand the pace and the annual singing around the village faded away. Then 'the opposition', the Anglicans, moved in. By way of contrast to the Church Synod, their singing seems to be Thatcherite and free-market. One evening is spent on the forecourt of the local garage – 'O Come All Ye Faithful' – amid the exhaust fumes as the commuters cruise in to fill their BMWs and Cavaliers. The second evening is a tin-rattling rush around the village.

Because of my liking for carols I also try to hear them sung for the whole Twelve Days of Christmas. This poses another problem. For some inexplicable reason many churches and chapels have discarded their carol sheets by the first Sunday after Christmas Day.

This year the Sunday after Christmas will be a church-free day for me. I will stay at home; the King's College Carol Service will be on the record player and I will be in full voice, with hot mince pies and sloe gin at hand. My carol-singing Christmas, at least, will still be in full swing.

56

New Year – Old Story

The new year has started in a miserable way. Despite public opinion and the encouraging words of my bosom friend John Selwyn Gummer, Britain's small slaughterhouses are still being harassed into closure by some of Mr Gummer's unsympathetic officials. In a recent reply to a Parliamentary question Mr Gummer said: 'The Single Market hygiene legislation is not intended to destroy traditional small businesses, which play an important part in the rural economy. My department has taken a number of steps to ensure that this directive can be implemented sensibly without imposing unnecessary burdens.' They are fine words but they evidently have not yet reached the Prime Minister's constituency of Huntingdon.

There, at Farcet, Tom Chamberlain's small family butchery business has just been closed down by MAFF after 101 years. His produce was excellent and he won 'Champion Sausage Maker' at the East of England Show last year. His business was flourishing and as he says: 'As far as I know we have never lost a customer, and we have never heard the word "recession".' Now, thanks to idiotic EC regulations, unsympathetic MAFF officials, a Minister who does not practise what he preaches, and a local MP, John Major, who appears to be deaf, Tom Chamberlain has lost ALL his customers.

On December 4th he received a list from his local MAFF official instructing him to make numerous structural changes to his premises by January 1st, or close down. No butcher can call the builders in during December, their busiest month of the year – but many of the required changes were absurd anyway.

He was told that he had to build a shower and rest room for visiting lorry drivers, despite the fact that most of the animals arrive

176

at the slaughterhouse from a distance of about five miles, by tractor and trailer, with clean, wide-awake drivers.

The slaughterhouse is about 20 yards away from the shop across a small courtyard. He was told that he could no longer carry the meat across the yard, a journey time of 10 seconds at the most – he had to build a refrigerated tunnel.

He was told that his pride and joy – a prize-winning traction engine that he takes to shows on Sunday afternoons during the summer, must not be driven past the slaughterhouse and shop – he must build a separate entrance for it. Yet when the traction engine is in motion the shop and slaughterhouse are locked up and not in use – what buffoonery.

He was instructed to build a wall around his garden so that he could not walk directly from his house to his business. He must leave the business, he was told, walk along the roadside pavement and enter his bungalow through the front door. The local MAFF official defends this nonsense by claiming that he is merely 'implementing legislation passed by the Brussels Parliament'. Mr Richard North, a well known food and safety adviser, believes that many of the official's requirements go far beyond the European Fresh meat Directive.

When Mr Gummer visited our farm he told me to inform him about any officials who appeared to be troublesome. I faxed him about Mr Chamberlain's problems well over a fortnight ago and I have not even received an acknowledgement; so much for our new found friendship.

Mr Chamberlain had another problem too. If he had kept in business he would have faced new meat inspection charges, increasing his costs in one year from £14,370, to over £55,000; an increase that no small business could carry in twelve months. My local Chief Environmental Health Officer says of the new regulations: 'I was happy with the old hygiene regulations and animal welfare standards. The new arrangements are overkill and most of the Environmental Health profession take that view.' Part of the 'overkill' has been caused by the Ministry itself. A rumour currently circulating suggests that the original European Directive was just 6 pages long. Our wonderful Civil Service turned this into over 60 pages of petty bureaucracy.

Our vet is another who considers the whole situation to be pure farce: 'There was no cruelty or poor hygiene standards. The present nonsense is just an administrative exercise simply because of the Common Market. It is not necessary for the little men; it's going over the top: I think it's rather like closing the pits down – all a bit hasty.'

Of course, the French and Greek butchers and slaughterers are not worried by all this – most of them will be continuing after the new regulations, just as they did before. Consequently I have a message for Tom Chamberlain's MP – John Major, you talk glibly about subsidiarity. Well, subsidiarity should start at home.

The other odd aspect of Tom Chamberlain's business is that nearly all the animals he killed were local. They travelled short distances and suffered little stress. Now they will have to be carried much longer distances to the few surviving slaughterhouses, with all the accompanying stress that will bring – doesn't this feature in the considerations of John Gummer and his ministry MAFFia men?

So 1993 could see the virtual disappearance of the traditional family butcher; the supermarkets must be laughing all the way to the bank.

My New Year's resolution is never again to read *Arable Farming* magazine. In the December issue a large farmer bemoans the fact that, if successful, a Private Member's Bill later on this month could virtually ban hedge removal in England. 'If action is not taken', he grumbles, 'this will leave a cost penalty to be lived with for ever . . . So with hedges, the motto must be, 'if in doubt, take them out.' Who said the hedge-ripping prairie farmer has joined the dodo; he is alive and well and in this instance is living near Driffield, Yorkshire.

A Peasant's Who's Who

Unfortunately, any book that refers to the real world must include the politicians and organizations who seem to live in the unreal world. Fortunately the 'sell-by' date of both is quickly reached, and these famous, powerful, singular and collective bodies drift into obscurity very quickly. Today's men can become yesterday's men, tomorrow. Phil Drabble once said something like that. He is a marvellous old forthright countryman made famous on the One Man and his Dog television programme. I mention him, in case he too has disappeared from the public view by the time this book comes out. He disappeared from the Any Questions radio dicussion programme several years ago for being too right wing, although the programme continued to have very left wing people on its panel; fortunately I take part in the programme under a different producer.

In case characters in this tome have vanished already, this simple *Who's Who* is just to remind readers who they are/were, as seen through my peasant's eyes. They are not listed in alphabetical order, or order of appearance – but simply as they float in and out of my mind; inevitably the one who floats in first is John Gummer.

John Gummer Also known as John Selwyn Gummer, John Worzel Gummidge, John Seldom Glummer and Johnny Gum – Secretary of State for Agriculture, Fisheries and Food for the whole duration of the Diary. MP for a Suffolk constituency he is also a strong churchman (Church of England) and member of the Church Synod. An admirer of Europe, but not of women priests.

Kevin McNamara A Labour MP for a Hull constituency. For those not acquainted with politics he seemed unexceptional, uninspiring and unknown.

Dame Janet Fookes A Tory Dame. I interviewed Dame Janet Fookes once. It seemed to me that she was suffering from the cuddly bunny syndrome and saw most animals as furry friends. I do not see all animals as furry friends, particularly the rat and hyaena. She was made a Dame after long service in the House of Commons. My mother had many years of service teaching, running a home and helping on the farm. She was not made a Dame.

Sir Teddy Taylor An amazing, bald, Scottish MP. Teddy Taylor once represented an urban Scottish constituency. His election could be said to have shown democracy at its best – government by the people, for the people. On failing to get re-elected in Scotland he travelled 400 miles South, to get elected in Southend. This could be said to show democracy at its worst – government for the people, by somebody else. Mr Taylor was knighted after long service in the House of Commons. My father, who gave many years of loyal service on the farm, was not knighted. From his urban Southend constituency Sir Teddy has waxed lyrical about farming, foxes and hunting. I have never written or spoken about cockles, whelks, winkles, or their most famous place of sale – Southend.

Tony Banks A Labour MP. From his Newham North-West constituency (to me an inner-city nightmare) Mr Banks has also spoken with conviction about foxes, badgers and all things feathered and furred. He is obviously a man of many surprises and contradictions. On one occasion I saw this great representative of the working classes at a station. He was dressed so nattily that he could have passed off as a stockbroker. But then with their large salaries, expenses and other interests, I suppose that many MPs are earning as much as stockbrokers.

   I spoke to Mr Banks once, through the phone fixed to my living room wall socket. He was using a portable phone on a train. I do not know if the possession of a portable phone is one of the signs of being working class these days. I have to say that I view portable phones on trains as being more anti-social than fox hunting or grunnit yurdling. Fortunately not many urban MPs have discovered what grunnit yurdling consists of and so they have not yet tried to ban it.

Sting A wealthy pop singer (at least he seems wealthy) who some people have heard of. He heard of Indians in the rain forest and wanted to save them. I do not think he has heard of me, and he certainly did not try to save my village when a motorway was planted right next to it.

Paul McCartney Popular mythology has it that this pop singer, ex-Beatle, was born in Liverpool etc., etc. Evidently he loved it so much that he took his fame and fortune down to the countryside of southern England. He is anti-hunting, vegetarian etc. If ever I become rich I think I will become a socialist, for then I will be able to afford all the political and philosophical luxuries I like. I will also become a convert to the theory that the moon is made of cheese.

Ministry of Agriculture, Fisheries and Food An entertaining organization that in the main manages to separate farming from the countryside, landscape, wildlife and conservation. For those wanting to get on well in the Ministry, I would advise an urban background, together with a degree in Ancient Greek or sociology.

Neil Kinnock A Welsh MP who was one-time leader of the Labour Party; he was once famous.

Roy Hattersley A Yorkshireman who was once deputy leader of the Labour Party – he was also once famous.

Tony Benn A Labour MP who passed through several incarnations. Once he was a viscount, then he became Anthony Wedgewood Benn, before finally settling for Tony Benn. Bits kept dropping off until apparently his name became politically and/or socially acceptable. Like Sir Teddy Taylor his interesting interpretation of the word 'democracy' meant that once the electorate of a Bristol constituency rejected him, he travelled north to become the MP for Chesterfield. He does not have a natural Chesterfield accent. To me this form of employment mobility has more in common with the football transfer system than with democracy.

Edwina Currie An MP for a Derbyshire constituency. None of my friends can tell me anything about her, as every time she bursts onto the television or radio, they switch off. My vet thinks she discovered salmonella.

David MacLean Another Scot who is MP for an English constituency. One of his constituents informed me that in his view young David's greatest political assets were a 'nice' smile and an attractive Scottish accent. My vet, originating from his constituency, wishes he would go back to Scotland.

Michael Howard Secretary of State for the Environment. *Dod's Guide to the General Election of 1992* does not include the Environment as one of Mr Howard's 'Special Interests'. My vet has never heard of him.

Jeffrey Archer Lord Archer of Weston-Super-Mare.

Weston-Super-Mare A seaside town in the South West famous for its donkeys on the beach.

The Royal Society for the Protection of Birds (RSPB) An organization which I belong to. It was founded over one hundred years ago by keen amateur naturalists. It is now run by enthusiastic professional naturalists, some of whom do not seem to like keen amateur naturalists. The Society's emblem is a black and white bird, the avocet. Cynics believe that it should be another black and white bird – the magpie. Unfortunately the magpie likes eating the eggs of other birds; there is no recorded description of a magpie eating the egg of an avocet.

Kenneth Allsop A fine writer and naturalist who is believed to have committed suicide because of his despair at the way in which the traditional English countryside was being wrecked.

Teresa Gorman Tory MP for Billericay in Essex. Speaks a lot of very good sense on Europe. Speaks a lot of absolute nonsense on the environment. I would like to like her but she comes from Essex.

Jonathan Porritt A pleasant, intelligent, likeable environmentalist. If I understand her correctly, Mrs Gorman views people like Jonathan Porritt as 'environmental terrorists'. In the real world it seems likely that Mr Porritt would find it difficult to terrorize anything, including Mrs Gorman.

Sir James Goldsmith A successful businessman turned 'environmental terrorist'.

Gordon Beningfield Yet another 'environmental terrorist'. Also the best wildlife and landscape painter in Britain. I say this because I know him extremely well and he takes me out to dinner. I have treated him too and he says that I am the best writer he has ever read. He left school at 15 and suffers from 'dyslexia'.

A. G. Street A wise and entertaining writer, farmer and broadcaster, known for his honesty and forthright common sense.

M25 A motorway ringing London designed to help limit world population.

All the other people in the book are vaguely similar to those already mentioned. To continue mentioning them and using even more paper would make me the direct opposite of an 'environmental terrorist'.